THE ECOLOGY
OF TOWNS

THE ECOLOGY OF TOWNS

by Alfred Leutscher

Illustrated by
Derick Bown

Franklin Watts · London

CONTENTS

**Franklin Watts Limited
1 Vere Street,
London W1.**

SBN 85166 520 9
© Franklin Watts 1975

Printed in Great Britain by
Tindal Press Ltd., Chelmsford, Essex.

INTRODUCTION

IMAGINE THAT your friend asks you to join him in a nature walk, right in the heart of his town. You might think that there was some mistake. With all the noise and bustle of people and traffic, what kind of wildlife could possibly manage to live in such a place? Instead of fields and woods there are buildings, streets and people. This seems a foreign world indeed for wild animals and plants to live in.

And yet, a surprising number of wild things do manage to carry on in such man-made surroundings. All they want is a place to live in, the correct food, and to be left alone.

This living together with nature has been going on for thousands of years, ever since our ancestors began to settle in one place. At first they lived as wandering parties of Stone Age hunters, staying in one place if game and food were good, and then moving on. In bad times they lived in caves, especially during the bitter winters of the Ice Age. Then, some 10,000 years ago, man began to settle in the rich valleys of the Middle East. Homes were built, crops were grown out of the wild grasses, and animals like the pig, cattle, sheep and goat were tamed. In this way men became farmers, and this way of life slowly spread across the world.

Today, from these small settlements have grown our villages, towns and huge cities like London, New York, Shanghai and Tokyo, containing millions of inhabitants. Down all the years of civilization humans have gradually spread through the countryside, building more and more homes, roads, and using more land for farms. Wildlife has had to retreat, with less and less room to live in. As a result some forms of wildlife have died out,

poppy

and others have gone to the lonely places for peace and safety. Surprisingly, some animals and plants have remained with us, and even manage to live as our neighbours. This remarkable living-together is what we can look for in our midst, right inside our towns and villages.

Wherever there is a chance to exist without being disturbed, some form of wildlife will turn up sooner or later. It could be on our very houses, or inside them, on a piece of waste ground, a rubbish dump, on the football pitch, the reservoir, or along the railway line.

This means that any naturalist living in a town can find plenty of interesting things to look for and study. Our homes are built in different surroundings so, to begin with, it is important to find out something about the neighbourhood and the type of soils and rocks on which our village or town is built. Is it in a sheltered valley or in the mountains, on the coast or inland? Is the ground soft or rocky, acid or chalky? Is it surrounded by woods or open fields? All this will give some idea of what kind of wildlife can be expected in the neighbourhood, and what might enter the town or village, given the chance.

A village in a woodland district will have plenty of wild birds about, some of which will turn up in the park or gardens where there are trees and bushes. Woodland birds will use these as a second home. A reservoir nearby will attract water birds which normally live on lakes, especially during winter. If your town is in moorland countryside where the soil is acid, then acid-loving wild plants may turn up along the roadside. They would be quite different from the chalk-loving plants which could be expected if you lived on the chalk downs. If there are pine woods near you, then you might see the shy little **Roe Deer** wandering down your road. It keeps mostly to conifer woods. In the mountains of Wales the **Horseshoe Bat** which hibernates in caves could be seen flying about over a village. There are some plants which only grow on rocks. If you live in a rocky district there may be plenty of walls built of the local stone. These should be covered with wild plants, especially mosses and ferns.

Wild plants in the village or towns will in turn attract various kinds of insects which feed on them, and even larger creatures such as birds to feed on the insects. Each plant or animal we meet is in some way able to live because it is adapted to its surroundings-its habitat.

This book is all about the **ecology** of wildlife in towns, how it has come to us, and how it manages to make a living. Ecology comes from two words, the Greek *oikos* for a home, and *logos* for a study. It is the study of plants and animals in their home surroundings, and how they manage to live together, in this case, with us.

My home is on the outskirts of London, which is nearly 30 miles across and contains some 9 million people. Even here we have plenty of wildlife. It could also be found in your village and town, if you only care to look.

ALFRED LEUTSCHER

seagull

5

BUILDINGS: TOWN LIFE

IF YOU look at any map, you will notice that most of the towns or villages are built close to a river or lake. The reason for this is that we must have water in order to live. Plants also need it, and animals will come down to drink at the river or lakeside. In a desert a water-hole or spring can be a life-saver.

When our ancestors first took up farming they settled in small communities near water, and in places where the ground was good for growing crops and feeding their animals. With a river these two things often go together – water and good soil. Up in the hills the beginnings of a river join up as tiny streams, flowing into larger ones, until a main river is formed. All the time the running water is wearing away the rocks, so that stones and boulders which break off are carried away. Slowly these are worn smooth, like the pebbles on the beach, and gradually ground up into fine particles. These mix with the dead remains of plants to form mud.

As the river enlarges and flows down towards the sea or a lake, this mud is dropped. Every time there is a flood it is spread over the valley floor to form a rich soil. It is this soil, the river water, and the shelter of the valley, that our ancestors were looking for.

A good river and valley to describe is the Thames. It was on the bank of this ancient river that London was born. Originally there was just a small settlement of Ancient Britons who were farmers. Then, in A.D.54, the Romans arrived under their general, Aulus Plautius, and built a small garrison. From this grew the city of Londinium, surrounded by a protective wall about one mile (1.6 kilometre) square. It surrounded two low hills, on which today you can see two famous buildings – on Tower Hill stands the Tower of London and on Ludgate Hill is St. Paul's Cathedral built by Wren. In between flowed a side stream into the Thames, called the Wall Brook. The stream now flows underground in the sewers, and a street runs above it.

This spot was chosen because the tide up the Thames stopped here before ebbing, and it was possible to ford the river. Today the tide flows much higher, and you can only cross by using London Bridge.

What did a Roman soldier see as he paced the city walls on sentry duty? The Thames would have been a clear river winding down a broad valley, and full of salmon. There were oysters and mussels to be gathered in the shallow water. The sloping banks would have been filled with reed beds, a home for the otter and bittern. Beyond this, on the higher slopes were patches of gravel in the shape of hills and terraces, forming a kind of heath-like scrub, full of birds and small game. Then, as far as the eye could see, the Roman sentry would have gazed on miles of dense forest, of oaks and hornbeams, growing on the thick London clay. Through the forest roamed the wild cattle, deer, lynx, wild boar, bear and wolf.

From this description an **ecologist** can pick out a number of different **habitats** for wildlife – a river habitat where the Thames flowed, a marsh habitat covered in reeds and willows, a heathland on the gravels, and forest on the London clay.

Today, after 2,000 years, the old Roman city is now a business centre of banks and offices, in the middle of a huge metropolis. Only traces of the old habitats remain. The river is now a highway for ships, and the salmon have gone. The reed beds and marshes have been turned into docks or made into reservoirs. Bits of the old heathland on the gravel and sand are now used as open spaces and commons. Only parts of the ancient forest remain as parks and woods, such as Richmond Park, Epping Forest and Ken Wood.

Over all this sprawls the mass of bricks and mortar, the buildings, roads and railways which make up Greater London. But in spite of all this upset and change of the natural habitats since the Romans arrived, there is still much wildlife to be found, as this book will tell you.

BIRDS ARE described as specialists in the way in which they live and are adapted to different surroundings. Some belong to water, others to bushes and trees, still others to open country or mountains.

In towns it is the rock dwellers which live on our buildings, birds which normally nest on cliffs and in mountains, or in rocky places. Probably one of the first to do so was the **House Sparrow.** No doubt our Stone Age ancestor knew it as a small bird flying around his cave and nesting somewhere in a crack among the rocks. The sparrow is a common bird in the Biblical countries, and is mentioned many times in the *Old Testament.* Today it lives in towns and villages and on farms all over Europe and Northern Asia.

Another familiar town bird is the **London Pigeon,** more correctly called the **Rock Dove.** Once a wild bird living on tall cliffs around the coast of Britain and Europe, it used to be eaten as a food. To make things easy the Romans built a kind of **dove-cote,** a tall and circular column of stones with holes in, called a *columbarium.* On this the birds nested, so it was a simple thing to collect them from the nests when a meal was needed. Pigeon pie was a familiar dish during the Middle Ages, when much of the food had to be gathered from the countryside.

Later, these birds were carefully bred into all sorts of varieties, such as the **Fantail, Pouter** and **Tumbler Pigeons,** and kept for decoration in dove-cotes in parks and town squares. From time to time these domesticated birds escaped, but instead of returning to the cliffs many of them went into the towns, to roost and nest on the buildings. This is how the familiar town pigeon has come about. Like its ancestor it prefers to live on bricks and stone, rather than in trees. A tall building is somewhat like a tall cliff and a railway station like a cave.

In late spring a small cousin of the swallow arrives from Africa – the **House Martin.** Once a nest builder on rocks, it now chooses houses and

fantail pigeon

builds its nest under their eaves. The birds return every summer to the same spot. To build or repair an old nest they collect mud. Each mouthful is mixed with saliva into a pellet, and added to the nest. The completed nest forms a rounded cup with a small entrance. Grass and feathers are placed inside to make a comfortable home for the young. When grown and strong enough to fly, the family flies off to Africa for the winter.

Starlings are very common in towns, nesting under loose tiles or in some gap in a wall. Holes in trees are also used. Whereas sparrows tend to stay in one area, starlings move about much more. During the day they forage for food in the gardens and fields outside town. Towards nightfall a curious thing happens. They gather into small parties and fly into town, to roost for the night on the buildings or trees in the parks and squares. One famous roosting spot is in London's Trafalgar Square. You can see and hear starlings every evening, flying around Nelson's Column before they settle down for the night. Perhaps they do the same thing in your town or village.

Every autumn there is a big invasion of starlings from Europe. They swell the numbers, and have been suspected of bringing over the virus disease of foot-and-mouth which attacks cattle. Starlings come into contact with cattle when they gather in the fields to search for grubs. Masses of starlings can damage and even kill trees when they settle for the night. To scare them off roosting on buildings all sorts of methods have been tried, such as making loud bangs, using bird scares, and putting sticky glue along the ledges. But they still keep coming back.

9

sparrow

town pigeons

10

starling

house martin

stork

An unusual sight in some towns is a beautiful bird-of-prey called a **Kestrel.** In open country this little falcon can be seen hovering over the fields, searching for prey such as voles. It will nest on cliff ledges and occasionally trees, but also on window ledges in towns. In such places its food is probably sparrows. I once found a baby kestrel which had fallen from the nest from a tall building in the heart of London. It made a delightful pet.

One bird which has long ago left towns and villages in Britain is the **Red Kite.** Although a bird-of-prey, it is more a scavenger; at one time it used to be a common sight in the streets, feeding on the heaps of rubbish. Now that we have dustmen and street cleaners, the kite has left. Today it is only found in the hill valleys of Wales. You can spot it by its forked tail.

You will notice flying around old or ruined buildings, such as a castle, a number of black birds resembling small crows, calling with a sharp "kia-kia". These are **Jackdaws.** In some villages and towns they nest on large houses with open chimneys, or in church belfries if they can get in. Usually the openings are wired over to stop them entering.

A jackdaw makes a most entertaining pet and is easy to rear as it will eat most foods. It becomes very attached to its owner. This is because jackdaws are social birds and live together. One of them is the leader and rules all the rest. Young ones obey their parents, and may become leaders themselves when they are grown up. If you raise a young jackdaw, then it looks upon you as a kind of boss jackdaw.

An old house near my home has wide chimneys where jackdaws rear their young every year. I found an abandoned baby and kept it as a pet. It followed me everywhere and, although it was never caged, it never strayed and used to sleep in a tree in the garden. I only had to whistle and it would fly down to settle on my shoulder. Being very inquisitive, it was always collecting things, and would even slip into neighbours' bedrooms and steal shiny objects. It had quite a store of trinkets hidden under a root of the tree where it used to sleep. One morning an annoyed neighbour rang up and asked me to remove the horrid black bird from her garden. It had hopped along her clothes-line and pulled out all the pegs!

On summer's evenings groups of dark-coloured birds with curved and pointed wings can be seen swooping and screaming overhead. These are **Swifts** which spend most of the time in the air, sometimes all night long. They come over from Africa for the summer and normally nest on cliffs, even high in the mountains. Within the past few years many towns have built tall blocks of flats, and on some of these the swifts are now nesting every summer. If you see some flying about in your neighbourhood and can follow their movements, you may be able to find out whether they nest on one of these tall buildings.

One of Britain's best known and commonest birds is the **Blackbird,** especially the male with his orange beak. The female is more sooty-brown. Normally a nest builder in bushes, the blackbird has found some most unusual places to nest in our towns. It can now even be seen and heard in the heart of our cities. One hen I watched in London chose a piece of scaffolding on a building site, using it like a branch. Another nested under the bonnet of an old, used car, flying in and out through the broken radiator.

How marvellous it would be to have a stork's nest on the roof! This does not happen in Britain, but can be seen in many countries on the continent of Europe. The **White Stork** returns from Africa every summer. People put up platforms or old cartwheels on the roofs of houses, farm buildings and even churches for the birds to nest on. People have watched the stork and other birds coming and going for centuries. It is even mentioned in the Bible – "The stork in the heaven knoweth her appointed time, and the turtle and the crane and the swallow observe the time of their coming."

kestrel

storks

14

swift

jackdaws

kestrel

15

NOBODY CARES very much for rats and mice. They do great damage, spoil our food, and can spread disease. Since the very beginnings of civilization man has been troubled by them, that is, from the moment he began to live in homes and started growing food. From then on the rats and mice have moved in, to live in our homes, in our farms, villages and towns, in search of food and shelter.

The **House Mouse,** a small, greyish rodent which comes out after dark, has travelled with man to the far corners of the earth. It has been carried in his caravans, carts, ships, trains and aeroplanes, even as far as the Antarctic. Like the rat it has been eaten by starving people, used in research, kept as a pet, and sent to the moon. It can live in most surroundings, and perhaps the most extraordinary mice exist in the cold stores in London Docks, where food is kept at low temperatures. They have grown an extra-thick coat against the cold, eat the food which is stored there, and use the covering on the pipes to make their nests. They are called "refrigerated" mice.

In spite of trapping and poisoning, mice still continue to survive, probably because they can eat almost anything, are shy and nocturnal, and breed rapidly. A female can have her first family when only two months old. An average litter contains five young, and they can leave the mother three weeks after birth. If shelter is good and food easy to get at, mice multiply alarmingly, especially in places like cornricks or in neglected barns and houses.

It is the same with rats, but on a bigger scale. At one time there were none in Britain. Like the house mouse they were brought over in ships. The first to arrive came early in the Middle Ages, during the twelfth century. This is the so-called **Black Rat** whose native home is in the Indian region. With it came a mysterious killer disease, called the **Black Death.** We know it today as the **Bubonic Plague** which is caused by a germ carried by the **Rat Flea.**

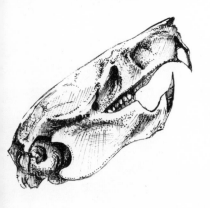

rat skull

There were many outbreaks of plague in those days, in villages and towns all over Europe and Britain. One of the worst broke out during the 1660's in London, when thousands died. Nobody knew the cause of this **"Great Plague"** but thought it came out of the air, and all sorts of strange remedies were tried out to prevent it. Ladies carried about little containers called **pomanders,** which contained sweet-smelling herbs and spices, in order to clear the air, but all the time the trouble lay in the houses and gutters where rats were living.

Sometimes the death rate was so high that horses and carts had to go round the streets at night to collect the dead bodies, and take them out of town to mass graves called **plague pits.** Perhaps you know of such a place near your home. If there was a death in the house the inhabitants put a red cross on the door, then listened for the rumbling of the cart over the cobbles, and the awful cry of the driver "Bring out your dead."

Today the black rat is a rarity, only existing in a few small colonies, mainly where there is shipping. It is now called the **Ship Rat,** and the odd one still comes ashore from abroad. It has now been displaced by a larger and more aggressive rat, the **Common, Grey** or **Sewer Rat.** This arrived during the eighteenth century, originally from Asia. It is bigger and bolder, and has a shorter tail for its size. Also, its ears are smaller. This rat can turn up almost anywhere, especially in deserted places where it can live and find food. This includes warehouses, barns, sewers, badly kept homes, canal banks, rubbish dumps, and food stores.

Damage to food alone is enormous. There may be up to 500 rats in a single cornrick or rubbish tip.

The reason why rats and mice do so much damage is not really their fault. Their curved front teeth, called **incisors,** never stop growing, so to keep them trim and sharp they must constantly use them by nibbling. It is up to us to protect our food, and keep down their numbers.

pomander

common rat

ship or black rat

house mouse

19

A PLACE TO HIBERNATE

DURING WINTER it is pleasant to sit by the warm fire when the cold wind is blowing outside and it is freezing. It is not so much the low temperature which makes us feel cold, but the moving air. That is why a sheltered place under a rock or bush, or behind a tree or wall, can give protection. During winter many animals need to shelter in order to keep alive. Unlike us many are cold-blooded, and can lose heat and freeze to death. As winter approaches, they seek out some hidden place under ground, beneath a log or stone or in a hollow tree. Slowly their body temperature drops, and the animal goes into a deep sleep called **hibernation.** So long as the temperature does not fall below zero it will stay alive, but only just. Next spring, as the temperature rises, it will wake up and become active again.

Because buildings give shelter, and towns and villages are warmer places than the open countryside, many animals will move into built-up areas for the winter. In Britain **Bats** hibernate, even though they are mammals and warm-blooded, and very active during summer. They can be seen flying over the houses at dusk, even well inside large towns, darting overhead in search of insects. By day they roost in hollow trees, in lofts, outhouses and passage-ways, and behind hoardings, anywhere so long as the place is dark and hidden. Their hibernation is spent in attics, church belfries, old mine shafts and caves.

This winter sleep is very deep. The heart beat slows down and breathing almost stops. The body temperature drops and the little animal's fur may get covered in dewdrops.

Many insects spend the winter in hibernation. Tucked away in some sacking in the garden shed, or even behind a curtain in the bedroom you may come across a sleeping **Wasp,** somewhat larger than the normal size. This will be a **queen wasp,** one of the young queens born in the nest the previous autumn. Apart from these young queens the whole colony of **workers** and **drones** dies off every year. Before she hibernates the young queen will have mated with one of the drones. Next year she starts a fresh

dormouse

colony by building a small queen's nest. This contains just a few cells. The eggs she lays hatch into grubs which she feeds. These become the first workers. As more and more appear they take over different duties. Some become the queen's nurses, others find food or tend to the grubs, some are builders, and others keep the nest clean and tidy. By autumn new young queens appear, to hibernate when the colony dies. Because wasps are attracted to sweet things, they enter houses to settle on jam and fruit. They may do damage to our fruit trees, but they also catch a lot of insects.

Some butterflies also hibernate. You can see them flying over a garden or park during late summer, and again in spring. Between times, they have been asleep all winter, perhaps in a shed or other building. Three of these commonly seen in towns are the **Red Admiral, Small Tortoiseshell,** and **Peacock** butterflies. A Tortoiseshell once spent the whole winter asleep in my bedroom, behind the pelmet. One spring morning it woke up, so I opened the window and it flew away.

There is one little winter sleeper which should be welcome in our homes, as it is a real gardener's friend and should be left undisturbed – the **Ladybird.** These beetles are easy to recognise by their rounded bodies, bright red or yellow colours with black spots. Ladybirds will attack the **Greenfly** which can harm the roses. They can fly and will enter buildings for the winter.

Some years ago the coffee plantations in Africa were being badly damaged by the **Mealie-bug.** Thousands of ladybirds were bred in a laboratory in England, sent to Africa, and set free on the coffee bushes. In so doing they helped to save the crops by attacking the aphids.

One of the most unusual animals to hibernate in my home was a **Dormouse** which a friend had found in a hedgerow. This pretty little creature is becoming rare in Britain, so I looked after it very carefully. As winter approached I placed it in a box, wrapped in a ball of hay, and it slept the whole winter through in the cold attic.

bat

bat

hibernating
tortoiseshell

TEXACO

peacock
butterfly

queen wasp

dormouse

MODERN HOMES are usually not built with cellars. These were once used for keeping the coal, or storing things. My house, well over 50 years old, has a cellar, and over a period of a year I kept a record of all the animals which used it as a place in which to live. They could enter from outside either down the coal-shute or through the ventilator grating. Even the smallest hole is enough for something to get through.

For some weeks a cellar beetle lived under a box. Called the **Violet Ground Beetle,** it has a beautiful violet sheen on its hard skin. Many beetles have wings to fly with. When at rest the hind wings fold up beneath the fore-wings which are made of a hard material called **chitin.** The ground beetle has its fore-wings, called **elytra,** joined together, and cannot fly. It is quite harmless and will feed on any debris it can find.

Fortunately there were no "black beetles" in the cellar. This creature should really be called a **Cockroach.** They live in dark and warm places where there is food, such as restaurants, kitchens, hot-houses and bakeries, and in warm animal houses in zoos. Cockroaches have been introduced from America and the Far East. They do not fly but run very fast when disturbed. Coming out after dark they forage for food, but will dart for cover when a light is switched on. Although harmless, cockroaches make an unpleasant smell.

A number of **Spiders** will enter cellars, or may crawl up the waste-pipe to appear in the bath or kitchen sink. In a corner of my cellar a **House Spider** had spun a funnel-shaped web in which it used to hide. I tried many times to coax it out by placing bits of food nearby. Only when I moved the food with a thin stick would it show any interest. This was probably because the spider hunts live prey and is attracted by movement.

Late in October I was in for a surprise. Moving aside an old suitcase I found underneath – a **Toad!** How it entered the cellar is a mystery, but it had good reason for doing so. Like frogs, toads hibernate and will seek a

house mouse

sheltered place below ground for the winter. In the countryside this could be under a log, in a ditch, or down a drain. I have a garden pond in which toads breed every spring, so the cellar must have been as good a place as any for spending the winter. Next spring it was gone, and had probably joined its companions in the pond.

There is something very remarkable about toads. Every spring they wake up, and start travelling towards a certain pond, usually at night. Only this pond will do and others are ignored. Nobody knows why they do this or how they find it. Some toads specially marked have been known to travel nearly a mile (1.6 kilometre) to reach the pond. My toad only had a few yards to go, in order to reach the garden pond, and fortunately did not have to cross any road. These migration routes must have existed long before the roads were built and today many toads get run over.

One of the friendliest little visitors in my cellar that year was a **House Mouse.** At first it was very shy, and darted back into its hole when I appeared. Later it became used to me and, if I sat very quiet and still, would climb onto my knee and take a piece of biscuit from my fingers. With patience and gentleness you can tame almost any wild creature. I gave it bits of newspaper with which it made its nest.

In a country house mice often spend the summer outdoors in the fields and hedgerows. After harvest when the corn is cut and the fields are bare, the mice find shelter in barns and houses. In towns where there is little open space they will live most of the time in buildings. An undisturbed cellar is just the place for a home.

cockroaches

25

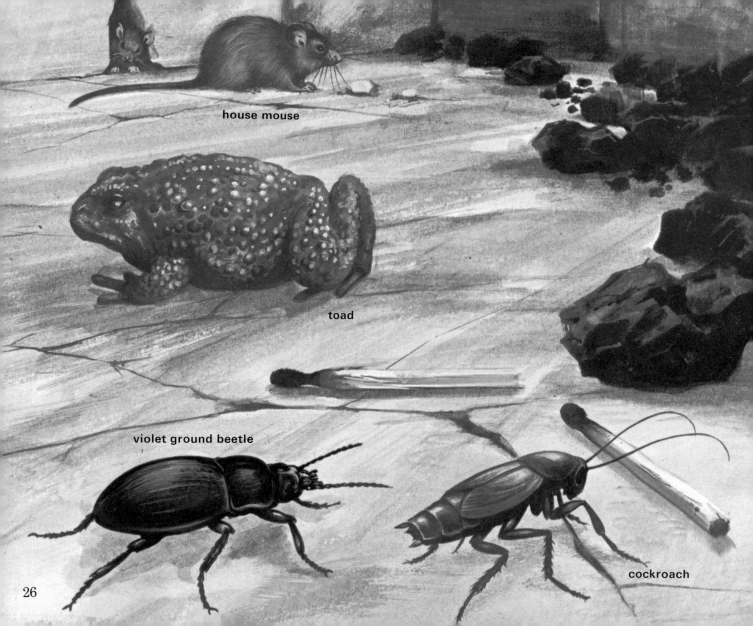

house mouse

toad

violet ground beetle

cockroach

house spider

27

THERE ARE a number of insects and other small animals which enter houses, and can do harm. One of the most serious is probably the **House Fly,** which has come to deserve the name of "Public Enemy No. 1". This is because of its dirty habits and the way it spreads disease.

The House Fly is about $\frac{1}{4}$ inch (5 mm) long, a mouse-grey colour, and has four dark bands on its back, or **thorax.** The two wings are veined, and the middle one has a sharp bend in it. Taken together these features should help you to identify it. The remarkable eyes are **compound,** being made of many separate lenses. This makes a fly very wary of movement.

Wherever there is a way into a building, flies will enter and settle on food. A fly has no jaws but a pad-like mouth which can only suck up liquid food. To soften it the pad is pressed onto the food, and a drop of **saliva** squirted on. To a fly the crystals of sugar are like large rocks, so the saliva helps to dissolve it. This is where the danger comes in.

Only a short while ago the same fly may have settled on some filth containing germs. This could have been a rotting animal body, on a rubbish dump, or on some excreta. Germs are picked up on its mouth and feet, and passed on to our food. The real danger is from human excreta, the solid waste we pass out of our bodies when visiting the toilet. Diseases spread by flies include **dysentery, cholera, typhoid** and **gastro-enteritis.** In each case the germs settle in the bowels and can pass out of the body of a sick person. A proper water toilet can deal with this, since the waste is treated at the sewage farm. If excreta is left in the open, say, behind a bush, by some careless person, then flies settle on it. This could start an epidemic if the flies then settle on food. Outbreaks of typhoid or cholera do occur now and then because of this, even in towns where there are plenty of toilets. Our best weapon is to make use of a toilet every time and to wash our hands afterwards.

Flies are difficult to control because they breed so rapidly. In warm weather a female can lay batches of some 150 **eggs** every few weeks, up to four or five times before she dies. These hatch into **maggots** which feed on

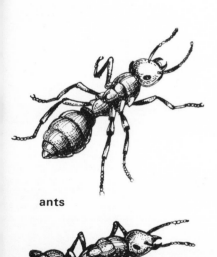

ants

rubbish or food, and then bury themselves in the earth to **pupate.** From this the adult flies will emerge. Flies can be controlled by using an insecticide, protecting food by covering it up or using a refrigerator, and by having clean habits to prevent disease from spreading.

Another annoying visitor is the large **Bluebottle Fly** which lays her eggs on food, especially meat. Here again, the meat should be covered up, especially in hot weather, to prevent it going bad, and to keep away the bluebottle.

Autumn is the time when **Wasps** are about. The worker wasps are busily searching for food, especially sweet things, and will make for the sugar bowl and jam pot. They do us no harm and will not sting, so long as we do not touch them, or go too near their nest. One way to remove a wasp is to pick it up in a cloth, and shake it out of the window. **Ants** are more of a problem. They crawl in through gaps under the door, or even up the wall through the pantry window. The only thing to do is to clear the shelf or cupboard and dust it with an ant-killer, and also block up any way in. Another unwelcome visitor is the **Clothes Moth,** a small, yellowish insect which suddenly appears crawling over some clothing or blankets. It is really its grub that does the damage, since the moth cannot feed, even though we say the clothes have been "moth-eaten". These grubs feed only on animal material, such as woollens, furs and feathers. In the wild state they probably once lived in bird's nests or animal dens. Cotton and synthetic material is safe. The way to stop any damage is to brush, shake or beat clothes or woollens, and to use the vacuum cleaner regularly.

Holes in the furniture are a warning that the "wood-worm" has been busy. This is really the grub of the **Furniture Beetle** which bores into wood such as shelves and furniture, or in wooden flooring.

Fresh holes on the surface usually appear in June when the beetles bore their way out. Shortly after they may lay fresh eggs. The wood should be treated with a wood-worm killer a little before they appear, in about May, and later in August in case there are any new grubs.

wasp

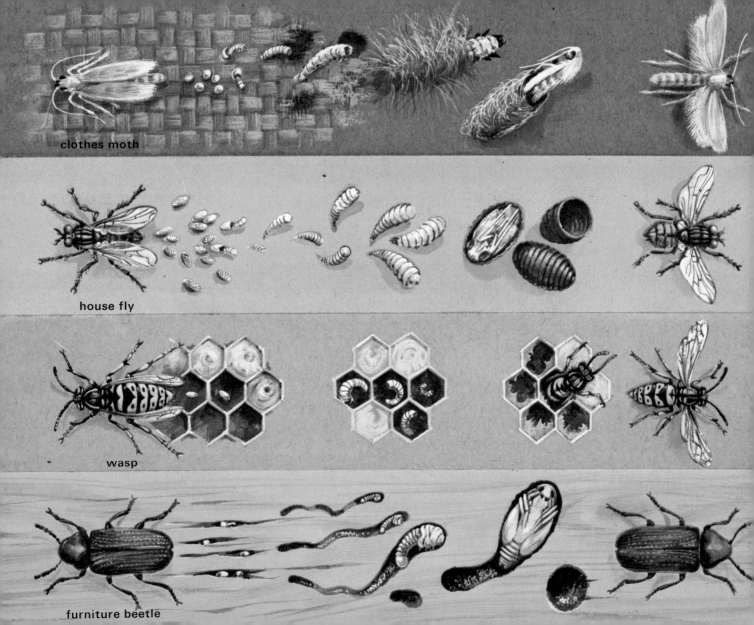

clothes moth

house fly

wasp

furniture beetle

PLANTS ON BUILDINGS

Normally the only plants we see in our homes are for decoration, such as cut flowers, or pot plants bought at the flower shop. Depending on where you happen to live, other plants may turn up on the walls and roofs of cottages or houses, especially in the rural areas away from smoke and dust. These are mostly **Mosses** and **Ferns.** Unlike flowers they do not produce seeds, but great numbers of minute bodies, called **spores.** These develop inside small containers, called **capsules,** a kind of fruit grown by these more lowly plants. In a moss plant the capsule can be seen on a stick emerging from the top. In ferns the capsules grow in clusters underneath the fronds.

A ripe capsule will burst and the spores will be carried away, sometimes for many miles. Some settle on walls and rooftops and manage to grow in the cracks, so long as there is a little soil and moisture to live on.

Some mosses and ferns can live in dry surroundings, but others prefer a damp and shady corner. Even in a large town you can find one or two, tucked away in a basement, an underground passage, or inside a drain.

A certain amount of light is necessary for these green plants, but **Fungi** can grow in total darkness. These are the strange plants which get their food from other sources, since they cannot make any. This could be on leaf-mould, wood, human food, and almost any kind of plant or animal remains. Fungi have none of the green colouring matter, called **chlorophyll,** which is needed to make food.

Like mosses and ferns the fungi produce spores, and these can easily enter the house. They settle onto neglected food and grow into **moulds.** One common kind is called the **Pin-mould.** It consists of a mass of white threads resembling some loose cotton wool. As it ripens, tiny black swellings appear on stalks, looking like tiny pin's heads. These are the capsules which produce the spores. The spores can find their way almost anywhere

patch moss

if there is a tiny opening, into food cupboards, ovens, tins and drawers. If something, like a book, newspaper, curtains, clothes, even boots and shoes, is left damp, then mould may grow on this also.

Another fungus which can do serious damage if not stopped is **Dry-rot**. It attacks woodwork in buildings where there is dampness. It has been known since ancient times, and the Bible describes it as "the plague of leprosy in the house". This disease could start in a builder's yard among the piles of wood, and the builder needs to watch out for it. In houses good ventilation is necessary, especially in a cellar which may get damp. Dry-rot can grow in darkness, and may not be noticed until damage has started.

Tiny spores settle on a beam or rafter and grow through the woodwork as long, whitish threads. By feeding on the wood the fungus can break it down to a fine powder. At one time wooden ships were damaged by dry-rot. On the surface the threads join into thick strands, forming into flat sheets which you can see on the surface. In this way the fungus spreads along a beam. It may even travel over brickwork, along walls, and under doors to reach another room. It has been known to pass on to the house next door.

When ripe, the dry-rot grows a fruit body from which more spores can emerge. When young this fungus looks whitish, then as it ages it turns yellow or orange, and later black. It should be stopped at once. Apart from replacing the woodwork, the fungus must first be sprayed with a chemical to kill it off and to stop fresh spores from starting a new colony.

Damp places and uncovered food attract all these fungi into the house, especially in warm corners. Try this experiment. Moisten a piece of bread and leave it in a saucer in a warm spot. Within a week or so a mould should appear on it, showing how quickly a fungus can attack uncovered food.

mould on a boot

magnified stem

moss
*polytrichum
juniperinum*

(showing spores
blowing away)

prickly shield fern

*(polystichum
aculeatum)*

dry rot

mildew

WASTE GROUND: A NATURE RESERVE

In every town and village there are pieces of waste ground which are left undisturbed, sometimes for years. Near your home there may be such a place. It could be the garden of a house which has been pulled down, a strip of ground by the roadside, an old gravel pit, or a deserted allotment. One day it may be cleared up or built on, but until then nature will try to make use of it.

At first there is bare ground, with rubbish left lying about – not a very promising place in which to live. And yet, after a short while, some colour appears as plants begin to settle. So long as there is some soil and water they will manage to grow there. Over the years the plants will multiply and increase in size, until the whole patch of ground is covered by bushes and trees.

I remember some tennis courts which were used regularly, winter and summer. Then the club closed down. That was over thirty years ago. Today, the courts are covered with a thick turf of grass, as well as bushes and trees, in some cases twenty feet (about 6 metres) tall. The place now looks like a miniature woodland, where once tennis was played. Now it is the home of birds and squirrels and a host of other smaller creatures. How has all this become possible?

The answer is that any piece of open, unused land will become a home for plants and animals to live in. If we steal the land from nature by building a road, house, railway, or anything man-made and then abandon it or pull it down, nature will return.

Over the years I kept a record of each new arrival, and it was interesting to notice the order of appearance. To keep a proper count I marked off an area 10 yards square with some stout wire fixed to corner stakes. Everything which turned up inside this **quadrate** was duly noted.

At first the tennis courts, made of hardcore, were quite bare and clean. First signs of life were little colonies of minute plants, called **Algae.** Normally these live in water, and masses of them can turn a puddle green.

moss
breutelia chrysocoma

Damp spots on land will also attract some of them, which can be seen as the green powder on the bark of trees and gate posts. One of these growing in a damp spot inside the quadrate is called **Pleurococcus,** a common one-celled alga. Under a microscope you can see its shape, and inside the tiny **nucleus** which controls its life. Around this is a portion coloured green, called the **chloroplast.** This contains the chlorophyll which helps the tiny plant to make its food.

Next to appear were a number of **Mosses.** Their spores had been blown into the quadrate to find a home on the tennis court. One of these is a moss called **Funaria.** It nearly always turns up where there has been a fire. In this case the hardcore of the tennis court had been made from burnt cinders.

As these tiny plants grew, spread and died, their remains helped to make **humus** which mixed with the hardcore which in a year or so was beginning to crumble. Then a number of **Grasses** sprouted. Here again, the wind had blown in their seeds from the neighbourhood.

By about the third year some **Flowers** were found. These were mainly common wayside flowers which can grow on poor soil and in a town atmosphere. Four of them were the **Plantain, Daisy, Thistle** and **Groundsel.** Plants like this may also grow on a neglected garden path.

The first signs of any trees were tiny seedlings from the nearby **Sycamore, Hawthorn** and **Oak** which grew around the tennis courts. This is the usual order in which plants will take over some waste land. First, the tiny algae, then mosses, followed by grasses, flowers, and finally trees. In this way waste ground may end up as a miniature woodland.

As soon as the plants have settled in, the animal life arrives, depending on the types of plant life which they feed on. Here are just three examples I noticed one morning. In a nettle patch was a colony of **Red Admiral** caterpillars. They are nettle feeders. On a hawthorn bush the **Bees** were busily searching the blossom for nectar, and under a small oak a **Grey Squirrel** was gathering nuts.

red admiral

37

FLOWERS OF THE BOMBED SITES

ONE OF THE most famous studies of waste ground took place in the heart of London just after World War II. A team of naturalists from the London Natural History Society went a number of times into the City where there had been severe damage caused by the bombing and fire-raids. A large area where there were once offices and shops lay in ruins. There were half-standing walls, piles of rubble and bricks, and basements and floors open to the sky. Here and there an air-raid shelter stood up, covered in sand-bags.

Many towns and cities looked like this in Britain and Europe before rebuilding started. Yet, within two years, the London bombed sites were covered in wild flowers, on which butterflies and other insects were feeding. Birds nested among the ruins, and even trees began to appear. This bombed site study was carried out to discover three things: which plants and animals turned up; how did they get there; once there, how did they survive?

To begin with, a plant must have help in order to spread. To reach the heart of a town a seed might be blown in on the wind, carried by animals or birds, on our clothing or vehicles, or brought in as food. Wind-blown seeds have parachutes or wings, such as the seeds of the **Sycamore** and **Dandelion.** Seeds with hooks, like those of **Burdock,** get caught onto an animal's fur, or on clothes. Hard seeds like those of **Plantain** stick to our muddy shoes or on car tyres and may be carried miles before they drop off. Fruits which are soft and tasty, such as berries, are eaten by birds. The seeds or pips inside are passed unharmed through the bird's body. If you half eat and drop a tomato sandwich, or eat a date or cherry and drop the stone, this is another way whereby plants reached the bombed sites. Many City workers take sandwiches with them for lunch. Quite a few surprises turned up in the search. Tomato plants were discovered growing among the rubble and also young apple and cherry trees. One summer's day I found a tiny fig tree, but it died later during the winter frost.

Some of the earliest plants to arrive came from the coast, mixed with the tons of sand needed for filling the sand bags. These were used to protect

bracken

warden posts, air-raid shelters and government buildings. As a result plants grew which are usually only found along the coast.

One successful flower which grew in masses in the cracks along the basement floors, was a long-distance traveller with an interesting history – the **Oxford Ragwort.** This cousin of the dandelion grows clusters of yellow flower-heads which produce parachute seeds. Its native home is on the larva soil formed by volcanoes in Italy and Sicily. This is a kind of dark, burnt soil. Specimens from Italy, probably from near Mt. Etna, were brought to England in the seventeenth century, and grown in the Physick Gardens in Oxford. As their seeds ripened they soon blew away, and plants began to appear on garden walls in the town. Next they appeared on the cinder tracks along the railway lines. Each time a train passed, the seeds were carried along the railway lines. In this way, over the years, plants slowly travelled towards the West Country, up to the Midlands, and towards London. Then came the Blitz, and soon the flowers were appearing on the bombed sites. The reason for this successful invasion is that the Oxford Ragwort likes burnt ground. First it was the volcanic soil in Italy, then the cinders on the railway lines, and then the burnt ruins in London. Even today you can see this plant every summer along the railways, or on burnt or waste ground.

Equally successful because it also likes burnt soil, was a tall and handsome flower, called the **Rosebay,** one of the willow-herbs. Its rows of tall stems carrying reddish flowers made a brave show along the tops of the walls remaining upright. Londoners called the Rosebay the "Bomb weed". As many as 80,000 tiny parachute seeds have been counted on one plant. Some days the seeds were blown through the streets, looking like a summer snowstorm. Also successful was the **Canadian Fleabane** which has silvery flowerheads. It has been here a long while: it was seen in London after the Great Fire of 1666.

These three plants were known to the naturalists as the "advance guard of the parachute troops". Later they were joined by many other plants.

tomato plant

Oxford ragwort

fleabane

dandelion

THE BOMBED SITE INSECTS

APART FROM all the flowers and grasses which reached the bombed sites, there were a number of trees. Their seeds came mostly from the nearby parks and squares. **Apple, Cherry, Plum** and **Pear** trees came from seeds and stones dropped by passers-by, whereas the wind carried in the seeds of trees like **Sycamore, Lime, Poplar** and **Willow.**

As a result of all this wealth of plant life, various insects soon turned up, to feed on the leaves and flowers. **Spiders, Beetles, Woodlice** and various **Flies** and **Bees** were recorded, but the most obvious and welcome insects were the butterflies. The **Red Admiral, Peacock** and **Small Tortoiseshell** butterflies were quite abundant, partly because their caterpillars feed on the **Nettle** which grew in many places among the ruins. More attractive was the presence of a bush called **Buddleia,** which grows clusters of small, bluish and sweet-scented flowers. It had spread from nearby City gardens. It is popular with gardeners, and sometimes called the "Butterfly Bush". One summer, in 1947, I passed a City bombed site, and counted fifteen butterflies on the same Buddleia bush. It was a wonderful sight, right in the heart of London.

Many moths were also seen, especially the **Hawk Moths.** These powerful flyers come out in the evening to sip nectar from flowers, hovering in front of them and using their long tongues as humming-birds do in the West Indies. Some lay their eggs on the leaves of bushes or trees, and are named after them, like the **Privet, Lime, Poplar** and **Convolvulus Hawk Moths.** A particularly handsome caterpillar which I found was that of the **Elephant Hawk Moth** which feeds on the Rosebay.

A more exciting find was seen in broad daylight. Every summer the small **Humming-bird Hawk Moth** migrates to Britain from Africa, and flies in daytime. I saw this one on a City bombed site, darting from flower to flower, hovering in front of each one and sipping the nectar with its long tongue. Then an amusing thing happened. Nearby was a coloured poster showing a picture of a bowl of flowers. The moth flew across and hovered in front of each painted flower, searching for a meal!

woolly bear caterpillars

Many more moths were found, including the **Pussmoth, Bufftip, Ermine** and **Tiger Moths.** The last two produce caterpillars with very hairy coats, called **Woolly Bears.** These moths are not usually seen, except by careful searching in the daytime. This is when they are asleep on fences, walls or tree trunks, marvellously camouflaged so that the birds cannot find them.

Some moths, however, show themselves with bright colours, and are easy to spot. The **Cinnabar Moth** has dark wings with big red spots, and its caterpillar is brightly coloured in a kind of football jersey of yellow and black rings. There is good reason for this. It is meant to warn away enemies because both moth and caterpillar have an unpleasant taste. Once a bird makes a mistake it remembers these **warning colours,** and leaves them alone. The caterpillar feeds on **Common Ragwort** which grew in many places on the ruins.

The usual town birds such as **Sparrows, Town Pigeons, Starlings** and **Blackbirds** were found on the bombed sites, foraging for food. One or two nested among the ruins, but there was one bird which caused a sensation – the **Black Redstart.** This is a very rare summer visitor from Africa which normally nests among rocks. Of all places in Britain it chose the London ruins to nest among. In one year, 1942, as many as 14 male birds were recorded. More than anything, this little bird goes to show how Nature takes advantage of all sorts of habitats, even man-made ones.

Probably your town or village was not damaged or so badly hit by bombs. Even so, if you find a patch of waste ground where there has been a fire, or look along the railway line you may see some of these plants which grow on burnt soil. I know of one City bombed site which has not been touched since the war, over 30 years ago, and the flowers still grow there every summer.

In all, the London naturalists found some 269 different flowers, grasses and ferns, 13 kinds of butterfly, 30 of the larger moths, and 20 different spiders. Many more insects were probably never found.

eyed hawk
moth

willow

buddleia

peacock butterfly

small tortoiseshell
butterfly

red admiral
butterfly

WAIFS AND STRAYS

IF YOU visit a piece of waste ground there may be some surprises waiting for you. Apart from the usual plants and animals which live there, some very unexpected visitors may also turn up.

One day whilst exploring the piece of land where there had once been some tennis courts (see page 36) I heard a faint miaowing sound from under some bushes. There, under an old settee which somebody had dumped, was a litter of new-born kittens about three weeks old. Their eyes were open. As the mother was absent, I sat down beside them and tried to pick one up. Immediately it opened its mouth and spat at me. A moment later the mother appeared, ears flattened and teeth showing, looking like a small and enraged tiger. Here, right inside London, was a family of cats as wild as could be. The mother was a tabby and I could easily have mistaken her for a genuine wildcat which lives in the Scottish Highlands.

And yet there is no connection. The **Domestic Cat** which we humans keep as a pet, or to get rid of mice, has been with us for thousands of years. It was first tamed and bred from an African wildcat, in order to guard the stores of grain and other food from rats and mice, all over the Middle East where farming first commenced. Slowly the domestic cat spread throughout the world. The Romans introduced it into Britain, whereas the wildcat, properly called the **European Wildcat**, was already there. A domestic cat gone wild is called a **Feral Cat**.

Throughout the Middle Ages cats were a novelty. This is probably why we always talk about London's Lord Mayor as Dick Whittington – and his cat. Not many people kept one.

Cats are very independent creatures, unlike dogs which need a master or mistress, and sometimes go wild, like the one described above. It probably hunted mice and small birds like its ancestors used to do. Now and then it probably went home to its owner for a good meal. They must have wondered where it disappeared to most of the time.

wild cat

Next day I returned for another look, but the family had gone. Later I found the kittens in another spot, hidden under an old mattress. The mother had moved them because her babies had been disturbed.

One unfortunate stray I found was somebody's **Tortoise.** It was busily feeding on some dandelions. This was fine. It was summer weather and it looked quite healthy. I found the owner and had to warn her not to let it escape again. Summer is all right, but winter can be a real danger. These pet tortoises come from warm countries in North Africa and Greece and, if caught by a winter frost, may die. A tortoise should always be kept in an enclosure from which it cannot escape, or in a garden from which there is no way out. When the first frosts begin, it should be tucked away in a box of hay or straw, covered with some sacking, and stored away in a cold but sheltered place for the winter – an unheated greenhouse, a shed, garage or cellar. It should be left there until it wakes up.

tortoise

A sadder occasion happened when I found a torn thrush's nest. The babies were lying helpless on the ground, and there were no parents about. Since they were almost naked and could not move about, I took them home and tried to feed them. I tried insects and worms, and made a mash out of egg and gravy, but one by one they died. It is not easy to rear such young song-birds. If you find one on the ground, it has probably left the nest. It is far better to leave it alone, or place it on a branch out of harm's way. Its parents are nearby, waiting for you to leave, so that they can get on with feeding. I would have done the same with the babies I found, but this was an emergency as the parents had probably deserted the ruined nest. I wondered who the guilty person was, a boy, a cat, or some other robber. Magpies, squirrels and crows will also raid bird's nests, and every year thousands of young are killed or eaten.

feral cat

magpie

wild cat

FOSSILS IN TOWN

As WE MOVE about the countryside, it is as if we are walking over a huge graveyard. Buried in the earth beneath our feet are the fossilized remains of countless numbers of prehistoric plants and animals. They are preserved in the rocks which have formed into layers over millions of years.

As the Earth's crust is slowly worn away by frost, rain, rivers and the beating of the waves, particles of rock are washed down to the sea. One day the sea may fill up and turn into a rock layer. Different layers can be seen in the cliffs along the coast. The size of the rock particles varies with each layer. Sandstone is made of a hard and coarse rock. Slate is also hard but smooth. Clay and chalk are soft rocks made of fine particles.

These rocks are studied by geologists who know their age and how they were formed. The person who studies the fossils, called a **palaeontologist,** can tell what each prehistoric plant or animal looked like, and how it lived and behaved.

It is like being a detective, hunting for fossils and using them as clues. Even in towns this is possible. In places where the rocks have been cut into, such as a sea cliff, a chalk or clay pit, a coal mine or a cave, fossils may be found. On the seashore fossil shells and even sharks' teeth washed out by the waves can be found, and in an old chalk pit often there are plenty of sea-urchins.

As you walk along the streets around your home, in almost any village or town, look at the pavement or the stonework on buildings. You may spot some markings. These could well be fossils which were buried in the stone.

London has buildings made of many different kinds of stone in which fossils can be seen. It also has fossils buried beneath it. Filling the Thames basin is a soft rock, called **London Clay,** which is many metres thick. It was laid down in the sea a good 60 million years ago. It contains shells of

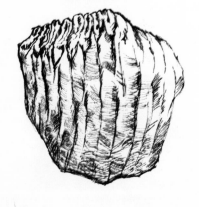

**molar tooth
of mammoth**

many kinds, shark's teeth and plant remains. When the new Victoria Line was added to the Underground, it went right through a bed of fossil oysters.

When buildings go up in London, or where there happens to be a gravel pit, fossils of a different kind show up. These gravel or sandy layers lie on top of the clay, and were largely laid down by the Thames. They contain remains of land animals. This happened mostly during the great Ice Age. Sheets of ice spread down from the north, covering most of Britain, but stopped just north of the Thames. Below this lay an arctic countryside of low hills, covered in winter snow for most of the time. **Mosses, Lichens** and stunted **Willows** were all that could grow. Arctic flowers bloomed during the short summers. Traces of all these have been found in the Thames gravels. Also remains of **Mammoth, Woolly Rhinoceros, Cave Bear** and **Arctic Fox** have been found. Fine specimens of skulls, teeth and bones are now in museums.

It must seem strange to a Londoner that where his home is now standing a mammoth may have wandered past some 10,000 years ago. There may not be any mammoth remains in your district. It depends on what kind of rock is underneath your village or town. A book on geology will help you to find out where the Ice Age animals and plants are likely to turn up.

You may even be very lucky to find traces of prehistoric man. His remains finds a flint tool. These Stone Age people were there long before the Romans arrived, when London did not even exist.

Fossils in towns may turn up unexpectedly – for example, a beautiful imprint of a fern leaf may be found on a piece of slate, mixed up with a load of coal.

shark's teeth

shell fossils

the sea during the Eocene Period

A RUBBISH DUMP

grass snake

IT IS SURPRISING what will turn up in a rubbish dump, if it is left alone and not burned or disturbed. In time animals find that it makes a good shelter, especially if there is food to be had.

Such a dump can vary in size from a small heap at the back of the garden, to the huge rubbish tip outside the village or town put there by council workers. Often, especially not too far inland, it has a crowd of **Seagulls** flying over it. They settle to squabble over the tit-bits of food. **Starlings** and **Crows** also hang around in the hope of a free meal. And there are **Rats!**

You can see all this from a distance, but it is *not* the kind of place you should explore. There are rusty nails, metal, and broken glass lying about, and sometimes poisonous substances. Also it is private ground. I was given special permission to look around, so can tell you what I found.

Apart from the rats and birds there were many flies buzzing about. During the daytime they attracted the swallows, and at night the bats chased the **midges and mosquitoes.** There were many plants already growing on the dump, mostly the common kinds. The animal life was more interesting, but mostly hidden between the piles of rubbish. To protect my hands I wore leather gloves, so I could turn over tins, pieces of metal and wood, and examine broken bottles.

Under one flat stone was a colony of ants. They rushed about rescuing their "ant's-eggs", which are really called **pupae,** and trying to hide them. I replaced the stone and left them to their busy affairs. In a broken bottle a spider had made her home. In the bottom were the remains of the many meals she had eaten.

The next discovery was a real surprise. Inside an old bath full of dead leaves was a clutch of creamy white eggs, all stuck together and about the size of pigeon's eggs. While I puzzled over them, the mother – a grass-snake – suddenly appeared and darted away through the rubbish. These harmless reptiles often make use of rubbish tips outside villages in which to lay their eggs.

Perhaps the most unusual find was inside a cracked and empty car battery. All the screw caps were missing, and inside one hole was the nest of a **Miner Bee.** This solitary bee normally makes a hole in the ground for her nest, but here was a ready-made home. In it she had built a nest of mud mixed with saliva, containing cells in which the grubs were growing up.

To discover further signs of life I used some traps and bait. The simplest trap is a bottle or tin sunk into the ground up to the rim. Small animals fall into this. To stop the rain getting in, and so drowning the captives, I put a sheet of glass or a flat stone over the top, slightly raised on sticks. Into this trap may fall various wood-lice, centipedes, spiders and grass-hoppers. Any one of these may be found on a rubbish tip. If sugar is put inside, ants may be caught. A potato cut in half is good bait for attracting millipedes, which are plant feeders, and a piece of wet sacking should bring up the worms. A piece of bread will bring along the slugs and snails.

Another interesting discovery was a **Cricket.** I could hear it chirping away somewhere among the rubbish. Today this is no longer a common sound in towns. Crickets usually hide away in nooks and crannies in warm corners, and there is an old saying "the cricket on the hearth". In the days when cottages and large houses had open fireplaces with wide chimneys, a cricket or two would use it as a place to hide in.

A cricket sings after dark, often a warm summer's evening. It is very difficult to catch and a baited trap is usually necessary. If you ever do see a cricket, notice that it has long **antennae.** It is also called the **Long-horned Grasshopper.** True grasshoppers which live in the open, among grass and bushes, have short antennae. They include locusts which can do so much harm when they swarm and eat the crops.

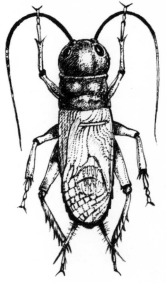

cricket

sycamore seedling

THIS IS the story of a tiny patch of ground, only a yard or metre square, which I prepared and watched at the bottom of my garden. On an empty flower bed I turned over the ground and broke it up into fine soil. Four stakes were put in at each corner, and joined with wire to make a small **quadrat.** On this soil I poured a number of kettles of boiling water, so as to kill off any life that might still be there.

Here was a lifeless piece of ground. Now it was up to Nature to see what use she could make of it. To begin with it looked like a miniature desert where nothing could exist. It was warm summer weather, and the earth was very dry. This is the reason why so few things can exist in a real desert. They must have water. Later on it rained, but by then it was too late. Winter was approaching and there was frost on the ground. When it gets cold, the soil animals hide away, or **hibernate,** and the plants die down. I had to wait until the following spring.

The first sign of life inside the quadrat was a tiny **seedling.** What would it turn into? I soon found out. As it sprouted, two tiny wing-like leaves appeared on the tiny stem. Actually, these were not true leaves, but seed-leaves, called **cotyledons.** They grow inside the seed and are nature's way of providing food for the baby plant. With a bird's egg the **yolk** is the food for the unborn chick. In a seed plant which grows into a flower or a tree it is the cotyledons. As these are used up and wither away, the true leaves begin to appear. This particular seedling was to become a **Sycamore** one day. The seed must have fallen inside the quadrat, blown in from a tree across the road the autumn before, and had rested all winter before it germinated. Most plant seeds need a rest before they start sprouting.

Next to appear was a **Snowdrop!** I then remembered that I had planted some in that very spot a year or two before. In spite of my digging up the soil and pouring on boiling water, the bulb had survived. Plant seeds and bulbs are very tough and can stand all sorts of upsets, yet still manage to grow. This one had survived, and now the leaves and flower were living up to their name, and growing through the snow.

When the snow had cleared, the next discovery was a **worm cast.** Digging carefully down with a small fork I found the **Earthworm** that had made it. It must have tunnelled into the quadrat and then come to the surface. Worms actually eat the soil, digest the bits of plant food it contains, then pass the waste soil through their bodies, to form these worm casts. This can be a nuisance on the garden lawn, although earthworms are of great value. The naturalist Charles Darwin called them "the tillers of the soil". By tunnelling they let in the air and also break up and mix the soil. This helps to keep it sweet and fresh.

An earthworm is worth a closer look. Stroke it from head backwards and it feels smooth to the touch. Stroke it forwards and it feels rough. This is due to numbers of tiny spines which help it grip the earth as it burrows. An interesting experiment is to keep a "wormery", a glass jar containing layers of different coloured earth. Some earthworms are put in, and the jar covered with a cloth. A few days later all the layers should be mixed up. Earthworms feed on plant material, so put in some dead leaves. Some of these will be pulled into the earth. When you see a dead leaf sticking upright on the ground, this is probably where a worm has been trying to pull it into its burrow.

An earthworm is an unusual animal, since it contains both male and female organs. Such an animal is called a **hermaphrodite.** When they mate and separate, each worm can lay its own batch of eggs.

Many more plants and animals turned up in this small patch of ground. As they came and went, I could see how a struggle for space was going on. Charles Darwin called this the "struggle for existence". Animals and plants are competing with one another all the time, and some will fail and others succeed in living. The "winners" in this case were the earthworms which took over the soil, and also the young sycamore. As it grew, it crowded out all the other plants.

snowdrops

OPEN SPACES:
THE ROADWAY
THE PLAYING FIELDS

ONE OF THE more unusual places to look for wildlife is along the roadway.

I discovered an interesting thing one very early morning when I went through the streets of Outer London, passing between houses, across a golf-links, and through a piece of woodland. During the night there had been all sorts of casualties along the route. I noticed one or two dead birds which had probably hit the windscreens of cars. There was also a run-over grey squirrel, a hedgehog, rat and a toad.

On my return journey the roads were cleared of bodies, as if someone had picked them up. It was the work of the scavengers. Crows, magpies and jackdaws had made their breakfast! Only the toad remained, because of its poisonous skin. Few animals will touch or eat a toad.

If you walk through the streets of your town or village at night, you may come across quite a number of night animals, especially during summer. There may be a number of insects, such as moths and beetles, flying around the street lights, attracted by the light. If so, look on the ground and you may see wings and other bits and pieces lying about. This means the **Bats** have been busy. Catching a moth or beetle, a bat will sometimes bite off its wings and hard parts in mid-air.

A real surprise to many town people walking home at night after dark is the sudden appearance of a **Fox.** It pauses to look at you (or you see it in the car headlights) and then it calmly trots away. Foxes have been entering towns more and more in the past few years, and seem to be getting more common, in spite of shooting and hunting. They can even be seen in the suburbs of big cities like Bristol, Birmingham and London. Since the disease of **myxomatosis** which killed off so many rabbits, the fox has had to turn elsewhere for a meal. It will even catch and kill a cat.

In every town there are playing fields. There may be a football pitch, cricket ground or golf-links near your home, where you could go and search for wildlife. If the ground is private, ask for permission first.

long-eared bat

In the longer, uncut grass, the plants grow normally to their natural size, but in the open part where the grass has been mowed they look quite different. Take a common plant like the **Daisy,** almost certain to turn up somewhere. Along the field border the flower heads of the daisies may grow on stalks up to four or five inches (10-13 centimetres) tall, reaching towards the sky as most plants do. Out in the open where the grass is short, the flower stalks may be so short that the daisies seem to be sitting on the ground.

As well as flowers there may be a few bushes around the field, one of which has been used for centuries as a barrier to separate the fields which were used for feeding cattle and horses—the **Hawthorn** or **May Tree.** It is common in hedgerows and can be trained into a thick hedge which is difficult to push through because of its thorns. The white blossom turns into red berries, called **haws,** and this is a valuable food for the birds in wintertime. In spring and summer the **Song-thrush, Blackbird** and **Finches** use it in which to build their nests. In winter a large thrush, the **Fieldfare,** comes down from the north and flocks of them will work their way along a hawthorn hedge.

Skylarks which like the open places nest in the long grass by golf-links. In summer the grass is full of singing **Grasshoppers. Moles** sometimes tunnel through the soil and annoy the golfers by spoiling the putting green.

During an evening walk you may come across a **Hedgehog,** looking for insects and worms. This friendly little animal is quite common in the outskirts of London, and likes to be left alone. If you finger it, it will roll up into a prickly ball.

Hedgehogs are fairly safe from dogs, but roadways are a great danger, and many get run over. So is the autumn time when they look for a place to **hibernate.** This could be a rubbish dump in the garden, or one made ready for Bonfire Night. When this is lit, the hedgehog may already be inside and so gets killed.

grasshoppers

fieldfare

molehills

blackbird

hedgehog

THE RESERVOIR

One very important thing we all need, wherever we live, is clean and fresh **water.** In days gone by it was a simple matter to fetch water from the nearby **stream** or **well,** because there were fewer people about. Also, the countryside was cleaner and the villagers did not have far to go. But there is always a danger to health, for water can carry disease germs. Also, if there was a drought, then the stream or well might dry up.

Today we take care to purify the water we drink, and also store it up so that it is always available. This is why near most towns we have **reservoirs,** which are large sheets of water holding millions of litres. Water is pumped into the waterworks to be purified, and then passed through pipes to our homes, shops and factories.

A reservoir is rather similar to a lake, a large body of water usually in some quiet place. Most reservoirs are built in valleys, even in mountains, by putting a dam across so that the valley becomes flooded by water from the river. A visit to a mountain reservoir can be exciting, because this is where the shy water birds gather, such as **grebes, divers** and **herons.** They are all expert fishermen. You may even have the good fortune to see the rarely-seen **Otter** playing in the water.

What about reservoirs near towns? Even here these shy creatures may turn up, especially the **Great Crested Grebe.** Fifty years ago this was a very rare bird in Britain. It was shot for its feathers to decorate ladies' hats. Today this grebe is protected, and almost every reservoir has a pair or two, even around London. If you see one, notice how it swims low in the water, has a sharp pointed beak, and a frill of feathers around its neck.

In a reservoir in London a pair of grebes have been seen courting. They circle around each other and "kiss" with their beaks in a charming fashion.

grebe on nest

Most reservoirs are stocked with fish, and each bird will catch one and offer it, or bits of weed, as a present to the other. The nest is built so that it floats. Each bird takes turn in sitting on the eggs, and will hide them before leaving by covering them up. Reservoirs are quiet places, apart from a few lonely anglers, and ideal for raising a bird family.

Sometimes a **Cormorant** may turn up, a dark fishing bird normally seen on the cliffs by the sea. In summer the **Swallows** fly over the water, catching midges, and a **heron** or two may be seen fishing by the bankside.

In wintertime, as darkness falls over London and many other cities, thousands of **Black-headed Gulls** arrive, to settle and sleep for the night. By day they are scavenging in London, or are fed by people. As the day ends they leave for the reservoirs (see page 86). At the same time the starlings are going into London to roost on the buildings (see page 11). They can often be seen passing each other, going in opposite directions.

Apart from birds and fish, and the occasional **Otter** or **Kingfisher,** there are swarms of insects which breed in water and provide food for the fishes. They hatch into midges and gnats which become food for the swallows by day and bats at night. Also, you may spot a bat flying over the water in broad daylight. This is almost certainly the **Daubenton's** or **Water Bat.**

A whole world of microscopic life appears at the surface, a kind of **plankton** consisting of minute plants and animals. This builds up into a large population for young fish to feed on. This can happen quite suddenly, and within a few days masses of tiny plants appear. This can cause the water to change colour. It can also be seen on many lakes. In Cumberland, on Lake Windermere, they call it the "blooming of the waters".

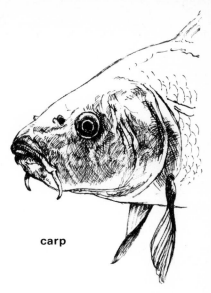

carp

kingfisher

great crested grebe

water bat

black-headed gulls

cormorant

tufted duck

heron

THE SEWAGE FARM

wader

WHEREVER PEOPLE gather in villages or towns there is the problem of how to get rid of waste material. This is done by sanitation departments who collect the refuse. Dustbin waste is collected by the dustmen, but liquid waste is carried from our sinks, wash basins, baths and lavatories, and by the drains outside, in pipes to the sewage farm. Here it is broken down and properly treated in such a way to make it harmless. It goes through a number of stages.

First, all the grit and solid bits such as stones, paper, rags and peelings are caught on a screen inside the **Grit Pit.** The dirty water, called **effluent,** passes into the **Sedimentation Tank.** Particles of matter sink to the bottom to form a **sludge.** Later this is dried and used as a **fertilizer.** The water now passes to the **Filter Beds.** These are filled with **clinkers.** The water is sprinkled onto this from above, through pipes with holes which move backwards and forwards, or in a circle. In this way each clinker gets surrounded by a film of the effluent. In this film grows a colony of one-celled plants, called **algae,** and one-celled animals, called **protozoa.** They feed and multiply in the effluent. In turn these are fed on by masses of small worms and insect larvae. These hatch into various kinds of midges and flies. As many as 40 million can exist on one acre of the filter beds.

The worms and flies attract a number of birds. **Starlings, Wagtails, Flycatchers** and **Warblers** are the usual birds to be seen, mostly in summer. In winter a number of **Waders** may turn up. These are the brownish birds you can see on the beach at low tide, probing the mud and sand with their beaks in search of food.

Finally the filter beds are drained from time to time, so that the water passes into the **Humus Tank.** All that remains at last is a fine sediment, which is usually taken out to sea and dumped.

Although such a place as a sewage farm seems so unusual for animals to find their food, it has a lot in common with the mud-flats along the coast and in the mouths of rivers. The bird life is somewhat similar, especially the waders. Many come inland for the winter, and will live on the sewage farm until next spring. Gulls may also turn up.

Plant life is often very rich, especially on the piles of sludge.

flycatcher

starling

flycatcher

pied wagtail

grey wagtail

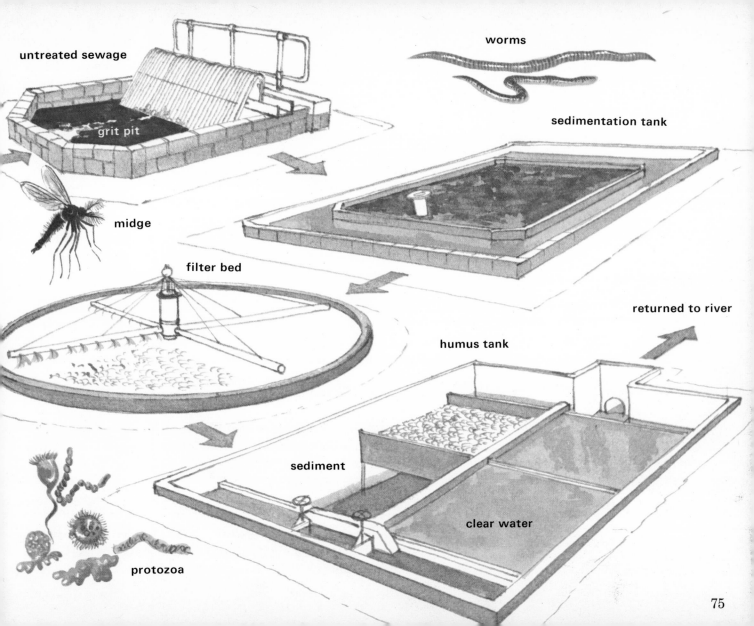

untreated sewage

grit pit

worms

sedimentation tank

midge

filter bed

returned to river

humus tank

sediment

clear water

protozoa

75

THE RAILWAY LINE

Up until the last century people travelled mostly by road. Then, in 1841, Stephenson invented his famous engine called the "Rocket". Since then railways have spread all over the country, to take many passengers and goods from town to town on some of the fastest journeys. Modern trains can now travel more than 60 miles (96 kilometres) an hour. However, there has also been a great increase in cars and lorries, and many railways on side lines have now closed down. There are now vast numbers of lines, as well as stations, which are deserted by humans, but not by Nature. There may even be one near your village or town. If permission is granted, a line like this is well worth exploring, providing you do no damage.

During a holiday in Devon one year, I walked along an empty railway line, to find out just what kind of wildlife was living there. On either side there were cottages and houses, with a town nearby; yet here was a kind of nature reserve.

First, I explored the small railway station. In the booking office a family of **Wood Mice** was living in one of the cupboards. The young were still in the nest. Wood mice are country cousins of the house mouse and normally live in the woods and hedges. They will also enter garden sheds, barns and empty houses, especially if food is handy. These "station" mice had collected a huge store of cherry stones from a nearby orchard, and stored them in the station master's desk.

On a window sill was a curious heap of oval objects, full of tiny bones and teeth. These were the food **pellets** of a **Barn Owl,** a beautiful, creamy-white owl which likes to roost in buildings. All these pellets had been coughed up after each meal.

Climbing the stairs, I looked into the upper room and was immediately surrounded by a swarm of fluttering bodies. I had disturbed a colony of bats which were all sleeping, upside down, along the picture rail! They were **Long-eared Bats,** and one of them was carrying a baby. Nature was certainly

baby rabbit

making full use of the empty railway station.

Outside, along the railway line the ground between the rails was covered with flowers. The famous **Oxford Ragwort** which got onto the London bombed sites was there and so was the **Rosebay** (see page 43). There were also patches of **White Campion, Red Deadnettle, Teasel** and **Mayweed,** and many more besides. As you would expect, the flowers with wind-blown seeds were the most numerous.

Bees were busily collecting pollen and nectar, and butterflies fluttered from flower to flower. One of these was the handsome **Painted Lady** which comes all the way from Africa every year.

I turned over a plank and underneath was a **Slow Worm.** This long and scaly, worm-like reptile is often mistaken for a snake, but is really a lizard and quite harmless. Like other lizards its eyes can close, whereas a snake's eyes are always open. Further along the line was a real snake, which I did not touch, but just stood quietly and watched—an **Adder**. It was basking in the sunshine, curled up on the warm railway line. A good look at this little British viper will show how beautifully marked it is and what a pity it is that people have to kill it. The adder is really a shy and timid creature, and will never attack or bite unless picked up or disturbed. It did seem odd to find it so close to the houses and town.

Still further on I met some **Rabbits** playing on the track. They had built their burrow along an embankment, and soon fled out of sight, except for one youngster. It sat still, unsure of itself, and I was able to walk up and stroke it. Then it ran for its life!

Even a great city like London has its wildlife along the railway lines. Many city workers travelling home along some suburban routes have had a delightful experience. On the embankments **Foxes** have made their home. Sometimes you can see the **vixen** and her cubs, sitting in a row, and watching the trains go by.

bee

bat

barn owl

wood mouse

rose bay willow herb

fox

teasel

ragwort

lizard

mayweed

adder

79

THE TOWN PARK

fallow deer antler

Most TOWNS or villages today have a park of sorts, where people can walk, sit and play, but it was not always so. Most of today's parks were once private property and belonged to large houses owned by wealthy people. Some even belong to royalty. In London, there are a number of Royal Parks, such as Richmond Park and Kensington Gardens. These are open to the public. Plenty of trees grow there, with shrubberies, flowers and open glades. Not so long ago sheep used to wander through Hyde Park, making this part of London look very countrified. Even more surprising is the sight of deer wandering about in some parks. At one time they were actually hunted, but today are kept for ornament.

One of the most attractive of park deer is the spotted **Fallow Deer** which came originally from Asia Minor. It, too, was hunted, but is now safe in our parks.

In a town park you are bound to see a number of birds. The **Blackbird** is almost sure to turn up, so is the **Wood Pigeon** which makes a flimsy nest in the trees. The **Carrion Crow** is also a tree-nester in many towns, but the **Rook** not so much so. Crows nest in pairs, whereas rooks nest in large numbers in rookeries and more in the country.

For some years bird lovers have been recording the different birds seen in the Royal Parks. In Richmond Park as many as 104 different kinds were spotted in one year alone. This is a park where you can see deer. Sometimes you can find a fallen **antler.** Deer shed them every year.

Where there are bushes, trees and flowers there are bound to be insects, even in towns. This is where some odd changes have been taking place, especially among moths and ladybirds. It is due to pollution. In areas where there are big towns and factories the colour of the tree-trunks has become much darker, because of soot in the air. As a result some insects which settle on bark have become darker as well. They have altered their camouflage so as to remain hidden from the birds (see page 112, the **Peppered Moth**).

Many of the trees in our parks come from foreign lands. During the seventeenth and eighteenth centuries many parks and avenues in Britain were planted with trees which were brought from overseas, for decoration. One of these is the **Plane** tree. It does very well in town parks and squares, and manages to keep clean because its habit of peeling off in patches gets rid of its old, dirty bark. From its branches hang clusters of flowers in the shape of round balls on stalks. The **Lime** tree, which came from Europe, has sweet-scented blossom which appears in June. The flowers turn into nuts, fixed to a stalk with a side wing, and get carried off by the wind. The **Sycamore** comes from the mountains of Central Europe. The leaves are very much like those of the plane tree. Everyone knows the fruit which has a wing shaped like a propellor, and spins round in the air.

Southern Europe is the home of two of the nut trees, the **Sweet Chestnut** and the **Walnut.** Because of our climate their nuts are usually small. The ones we buy at Christmas come from Spain and Italy.

Some parks contain the **Oak** tree which is a true native. Some fine old oaks must be up to 300 years old. Every year there are masses of acorns for the squirrels to gather.

If you collect some of these fruits from the trees in your park it is possible to grow little trees in flower pots. Acorn, walnut, chestnut and the fruits of the lime, sycamore and hawthorn will all turn into seedlings and may grow for years. Give them some good soil and do not forget to water them.

oak seedling

wood pigeon

carrion crow

oak

beech

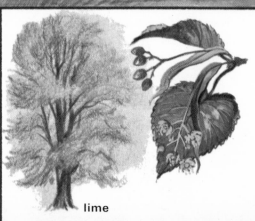

lime

fallow deer

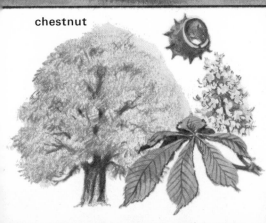

chestnut

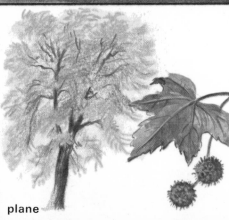

plane

walnut

THE TOWN LAKE

In almost every town or village there is a pond or lake, which was built for a purpose. The village pond probably started as a place where cattle could come to drink and where the ducks and geese were kept. More important was the pond which was built along one of the coach roads. This is where the horses could stop to rest and drink during the long and dusty journeys. Village life was usually centred on the village green with its pond and a handy inn close by.

Today such ponds are mostly kept for ornament, and some of the prettiest villages would not be complete without one. In towns there is usually a lake of some kind in the park, all part of somebody's estate years ago. Now the public can use it for boating or to feed the various ducks, geese and swans.

Many of these are foreign birds, but cannot fly away because their wings are clipped. To a naturalist the wild birds that turn up now and then are more interesting. This happens more in wintertime when wild water birds come inland for shelter. The **Black-headed Gull** we have already met does this every day during winter and is now a familiar sight. However its black cap is missing because this is only a summer dress. Look for the dark smudge behind each eye, which is all of it that remains during winter, and also the reddish beak and feet. By day this gull remains in town but every evening flies off to roost on the reservoirs (see page 71).

Where do they go in summer? By catching gulls and placing a ring with a number and address on one leg, it has been discovered that the gulls in London fly off to the marshy places around lakes and lochs in Northern England and Scotland. Some even cross the North Sea and nest along the shores of the Baltic. Colonies of **Black-headed Gulls** nest on the ground and

black-headed gulls

are not really sea-birds. Next winter they are back again, and you may spot a gull here and there with a ring on its leg.

Even some of the **Mallards** which appear so tame are really wild. Standing on one of the bridges over the Thames in early morning you can see small flocks of them coming up river to visit the lakes in the parks, and at dusk returning downriver to the mud-flats where they spend the night.

Occasionally in a severe winter you may spot a water bird which seldom comes into a town. We all know the ordinary **Mute Swan** with its graceful, curved neck. Have you ever seen a truly wild swan? The **Bewick Swan** is wild and goes up to the Arctic to breed. In winter it comes back to rest on quiet lakes in Scotland and Northern England. One winter I spotted one on the Round Pond in Kensington Gardens, right inside London.

Lakes and ponds in towns also contain fish as well as other water creatures. These could be native fishes, ranging in size from the little **Stickleback** to the giant **Carp,** or even **goldfish** in some smaller pool.

The **Old English Carp,** as it is sometimes called, is not really a true native, but was introduced from Asia during the Middle Ages. It was usually kept in special ponds in monastery gardens only. This was because of Christian beliefs that only fish should be eaten on a Friday.

Whereas the carp has hardly changed from its ancestor, the **goldfish** is quite different. Years ago the Chinese, and later the Japanese, bred the goldfish from another wild carp found in Asia, rather dull and greenish-bronze in colour. After many years of careful breeding the gold colour was produced, and also different shapes, especially the fins, but baby goldfish always start their lives the same dark colour as their ancestors. Each kind has been given a name, such as the **Veiltail, Fantail, Shubunkin** and many others.

mallard

mallard

Canada goose

mute swan

moor hen

THE CAR PARK

WITH MORE and more cars on the road it has become necessary for every town and village to have a car park. Although cars are coming and going all the time in such a busy place, it is always possible to find some kind of wildlife.

A lot of night insects, as well as plant seeds, are picked up by moving cars, and stick to the bonnet or windscreen. Apart from the various midges, gnats, moths, beetles, as well as wasps and bees, there may even occasionally be a dead bat.

An entomologist once found a rare moth "caught" by his car. Thinking back over his route, he went back, and found many more at a certain spot. This is now one of the very few places where this moth is found and is wisely kept a secret.

When the car park is dark, a car with its lights on will attract all the night-flying insects flying about. For example, the **Swallowtail** moth, coloured a pale, creamy yellow, is often about in towns and will enter open windows. Another is a **Garden Tiger** moth. This is brightly coloured in black and red, with white spots. Its hairy "woolly bear" caterpillar feeds on nettle, and probably there will be a large patch of this by the car park. When touched the caterpillar will curl up like a hedgehog, and few birds will eat it.

There may also be a **Cockchafer** or **Maybug.** This beetle can be heard on a quiet evening as it buzzes past, making a droning noise with its wings. Its large, white grubs which live in the soil feed on grass roots, and can sometimes damage a farmer's meadow.

cockchafer

In a car park I know is a fine old horse chestnut tree, and every spring the sticky buds burst into leaf, and later the bunches of white flowers, called "candles", appear. Then the tree looks a real picture. Most mornings the tree is occupied by a pair of unusual doves, smaller and more slender than the wood pigeon. These are **Collared Doves** and look similar to **Turtle Doves,** but with a black collar behind the neck. This dove has come over from the Continent in recent years. The first pair were seen on the Norfolk coast in 1955. Since then they have spread all over Britain, and live in loose colonies where there is suitable food, such as grain. Also they prefer to nest in conifer trees. It so happens there are some cedar trees near this particular car park in which they nest. Also, people feed them. Collared doves seem unafraid of humans and are now living in villages and the outskirts of large towns. Perhaps you have some where you live.

This car park has a lamp standard near the entrance which lights up in the evening. The stand is hollow, and I noticed one morning a small bird fly up with a beakful of nest material, and disappear inside the standard. It was a **Blue Tit.** That year it successfully raised a family, in spite of all the noise of cars and people passing by every day. Years ago in the old gas-lamp days, this was a common thing, when blue tits often nested inside the lanterns.

horse chestnut

collared dove

blue tit

swallowtail moth

garden tiger
moth

A BOTTLE GARDEN

How MANY of the smaller animals do we ever see as we walk to school or work? Even in towns there is much to find and study. Hidden against a wall or tree-trunk may be a **Moth,** beautifully camouflaged, yet right by the road-side. Nobody has seen it. Under a stone is hidden a sleeping **Snail.** It will only come out at night or after rain. In the rubbish dump we pass, a whole host of **Woodlice, Spiders** and **Centipedes** live and feed on all the debris and rotten pieces of wood. **Earthworms** are just under the turf on any patch of grass. On a piece of waste ground is a young **Sycamore** tree. The winged fruit blew in two years ago from the big tree opposite the house. Down the drain in the road outside a **Fern** is growing against the wet brick-work. These could be some of the living things around your home.

Because they do not move about much it is possible to keep them for a while in a glass or plastic container. There are plenty of plastic boxes about, or you could use a large glass jar. This can be made into a very attractive home for small plants and animals—a kind of bottle garden. I make use of an old glass aquarium. You need a container you can see through, and which will keep in the damp. This is important, since most small animals like to hide in dark and damp places.

To make the garden, first give the container a good wash and clean. On the bottom sprinkle some soil and place on this a few dead leaves and twigs. One or two flat stones or pieces of bark will make good hiding places. Make it all look like a normal piece of ground.

The plants you then require are those which grow in damp and shady corners, such as mosses and small ferns. Some of these can be obtained from

moth camouflaged
on bark

the flower shop, but they must be small as there is not much room in your garden. If there is a space, sink a shallow glass dish and fill it with clean water, to make a miniature pond. A tin lid would do.

Mosses are not hard to find. It is best to find some already growing on a piece of bark or stone: then they will live longer. Plant one or two small ferns, and your bottle garden should now look like a tiny piece of the country-side.

It should be covered with a sheet of plastic or glass, slightly raised on supports, such as pieces of wood or plasticine, so that there is a slight gap. This will let in air, but will keep in the dampness. Also, it keeps out the dust—and the cat! Place your garden in a shady corner.

For animals you collect any of those which may turn up in the rubbish dump. It might be best to try out one or two at a time, say, a snail or two, some millepedes or woodlice. These are all vegetarians, so will not attack one another. So that they will leave the plants alone, give them small pieces of lettuce or cabbage to eat, or a slice of apple or raw potato. The woodlice will prefer some old wood.

A garden spider should be kept by itself, and may even spin a web. You could then give it flies you have caught, by placing them on the web.

There is no reason why you should not have a whole row of these bottle gardens, so that the small animals can be kept apart, each in its own home. As you watch them you may notice that they keep away from the light, and usually come out when it is dark, or if you sprinkle the plants with water. Make sure the garden never gets too dry. A torch is useful to have, so that you can examine the animals when the room is dark. They do not hide away simply to avoid enemies, but because Nature has given them an instinct to move away from the light.

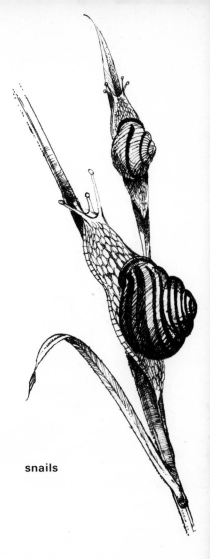

snails

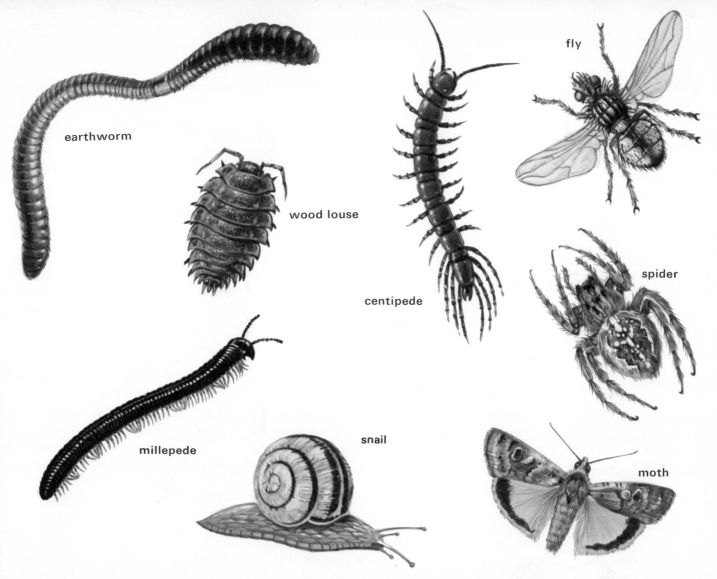

earthworm

wood louse

fly

centipede

spider

millepede

snail

moth

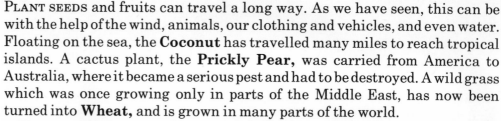

A FREE LIFT

PLANT SEEDS and fruits can travel a long way. As we have seen, this can be with the help of the wind, animals, our clothing and vehicles, and even water. Floating on the sea, the **Coconut** has travelled many miles to reach tropical islands. A cactus plant, the **Prickly Pear,** was carried from America to Australia, where it became a serious pest and had to be destroyed. A wild grass which was once growing only in parts of the Middle East, has now been turned into **Wheat,** and is grown in many parts of the world.

These particular long-distance travellers have gone far, but this journeying goes on all the time, even for short distances. It is Nature's way of spreading plants so that they do not become overcrowded. However, as the Bible says, if the seed falls on stony ground it may not germinate. The soil must be the right kind to suit the particular seed—hard or loose, wet or dry, acid or chalky, in shade or in sunlight.

Places like this exist everywhere, and plants find them sooner or later. Even in a town you can try out some experiments, to see how seeds are spread, and where they will then grow. I remember once blowing a **Dandelion** "clock", and then following one of the tiny parachute seeds as it drifted away on the wind. The journey started from my front garden, where a dandelion plant was growing. The seed was carried over the front hedge, along the pavement, and got caught up on a tree trunk. I waited until a gust of wind took it off towards the main road, and blew it onto the platform of a stationary bus. So I jumped on, paid my fare, and told the conductor I would get off when the dandelion seed did! Two stops later it blew away and I followed it onto the village green where it finally settled in the grass. I marked the spot, and next year a young dandelion plant was growing. It is now a healthy, three-year old parent, and must have sent off thousands of its own seeds on journeys like this. Following a dandelion seed is not too easy and you must watch your step, so be careful if you try it.

dandelion clock

96

Easier is to see how far away a **Sycamore** seed will travel as it spins through the air. Try it from an upstairs room. Let the seed blow away, and see how far it travels. You could also do the same with an acorn or a "conker". If you know a place where an **Oak** or **Chestnut** tree is growing on its own, have a look around it, and you may find a number of seedlings or young trees. Of course, the squirrels are a great help when they bury acorns, and they must have planted thousands of trees in this way.

Find the seeds of a plant which has hooks, such as the **Burdock, Goose-grass** or **Thistle.** Fix one onto your clothes or on your dog, and go for a walk. You could then walk quite a distance before it falls off. Another experiment is with a hard, nut-like seed from a plant such as the **Plantain** or **Buttercup.** You could also try some seeds from a packet of bird seed. Fix this to some mud on your shoes or football boot when you do not need it. Leave the shoe in the cupboard, but keep on examining it to see how long it takes for the mud to dry and the seed to fall off. If you had been using the shoe, the seed might have dropped off a long way from home.

In every case, you see where your seed ends up, mark the spot and go back later to see whether it has taken root. As the shoot appears you will notice the cotyledon leaves (see page 60). They are used up as food for the baby seedling. This gives it a good start in life, before the true leaves appear.

A good way to watch a seed grow is with a glass jar. Inside this place a roll or blotting paper so that it presses against the glass. Pour in some water so that it is kept wet. Between the glass and blotting paper place a fresh bean or pea seed and keep it for a while in the dark. Soon the root will appear, and then the shoot with the two cotyledons. Try this with two or three seeds. You will find that in whatever position you place them, the shoot will always grow upwards and the root downwards. The shoot makes for the light, that is, above ground, and the root for the darkness in the soil.

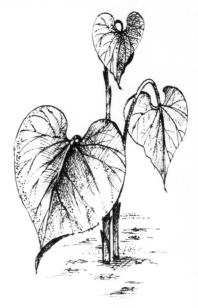

bean seedling

OWL PELLETS

roosting tawny owl

Owls are birds-of-prey which hunt mainly by night. They are covered with soft feathers and fly on silent wings. Their large eyes are made to see well, being placed in front of the head for a good view. Because its eyes are fixed and cannot move, an owl is able to turn its head completely round, and look behind it without twisting its body. Actually, it is the hearing of an owl which is so keen. It can hear the slightest sound, even the faint rustling of a mouse in the undergrowth. You cannot see its ears, since their openings are hidden beneath the feathers.

To catch its prey an owl pounces on its victim and holds it with its strong clawed feet. If small enough, the prey is swallowed whole; otherwise pieces are torn off with the hooked beak. Apart from the flesh, even the fur or feathers, as well as pieces of bone, are swallowed.

The owl most likely to turn up in your town or village is the **Brown** or **Tawny Owl.** It is really a woodland bird which roosts in trees and rears its young in a hollow tree-trunk. Because there are many trees in towns, in the parks and gardens, there may well be tawny owls in your neighbourhood. Perhaps you have heard one hooting at night, or seen one asleep in a tree. When all the garden birds get excited and all start their alarm cries, perhaps they have found one and are mobbing it.

When an owl swallows food, the parts it cannot digest are coughed up as a **food-pellet.** If you know where an owl is roosting, see if you can find some pellets lying on the ground. They are sausage-shaped and about the size of a boy's thumb. Take some home and soften them in a bowl of warm water. This will separate the contents. Remove these through a strainer and dry them between some blotting paper or newspaper.

You will now have an interesting collection of bones, teeth, skulls and fur of the small animals which the owl has eaten. They will be such creatures as mice, shrews, and voles. There may also be a few remains such as feathers of small birds, although the tawny owl usually does not catch birds. Also, there may be the hard remains of beetles.

With some glue you can arrange your collection by sticking the pieces onto a sheet of white cardboard, and even try to name each part. Perhaps a naturalist friend or the local museum can help you. In this way you can work out what the owl in your village or town has been feeding on.

At one time owls were treated as vermin and many were shot or trapped because people thought that they hunted songbirds and farm birds. Now we know better. They mainly hunt and catch large numbers of small mammals, such as mice and voles. Owls in Britain are now protected.

We sometimes talk about the "wise old owl", because of its large and solemn eyes. Actually owls are not very intelligent, and their babies in particular are rather helpless. They frequently fall out of the tree before they can properly fly, and are likely to die. Many people have picked up a baby owl and reared it as a pet. This is not too difficult. I once brought up such a baby tawny owl, and it grew into a lovable pet, quite tame and friendly.

At first it was helpless and had to be fed by hand. In feeding an owl it is important to include some fur or feather with each meal, in order to keep it healthy. Bare pieces of raw meat are not enough. The butcher let me have the odd bits, like chicken heads and rabbit's feet. We also fed it dead mice, caught by helpful neighbours. In its cage we found plenty of food pellets.

Sometimes you will read in the newspaper that someone has been attacked by an owl. This usually happens to somebody who comes too near to the tree where its babies are hidden. A man was waiting at the bus stop one morning, when an owl suddenly flew down and knocked his hat off. The tree with the nest hole was only a few yards away, right by the main road.

shrew

tawny owl

OWL PELLET

convolvulus

A LINE TRANSECT

When a botanist wishes to make a study of a piece of land, to see what kind of plants are growing there, he can do so by making a plan, and marking in their positions. By counting the numbers of different plants he gets some idea of those which are common or rare. This may have something to do with the kind of soil on which the plants grow, or be due to some disturbance where someone has been digging, had a fire, or be a place where people walk a lot such as a footpath. The grass may have been mown or a bird may have dropped a seed. All these things will determine which plants you will find.

One way to study this kind of **ecology** is to make a **line transect.** This simply means, to stretch a piece of long string or wire in a straight line along the ground, tied to stakes, and then work along this to see which plants you come across. This can all be put down on paper as a drawing.

On the next two pages is an example of such a transect which I made in London. I chose a line across some waste ground. It crossed part of an old allotment, then went over a footpath, across a ditch and through a hedge, over some burnt ground where there had been a bonfire, and finally across a fallen tree.

On the dry allotment soil were a number of plants of waste ground we have already met, such as **Dandelions, Mayweed, Couch Grass** and **Creeping Buttercup.** The last two can be a nuisance in the garden, since they creep along the ground and are not easy to remove. Couch grass has a stem, or **rhyzome,** which grows below ground, and the buttercup has one just above. It keeps on rooting as it grows, sending up fresh shoots.

Across the path only a few plants managed to stand up to the footsteps of passers-by, such as the **Plantain, Daisy** and **Thistle** which can hug the ground. On the open playing field they (see page 65) grow as flat rosettes.

In the ditch were a number of moisture-loving plants that like to grow in shade. These included the **Lesser Celandine** (a cousin of the buttercup), a few **Mosses,** and a **Male Fern** which is commonly found in woods.

The transect then crossed through the hedge at a point where an **Elderberry** bush was growing. This very common tree is so tough that it can even grow on rubbish tips and on slag heaps. Country people gather the white blossom or the black berries to make elderberry wine. On a branch I discovered a strange fungus called the Jew's-ear, which nearly always grows on this particular tree. It is cup-shaped, soft and fleshy to the touch, and shaped like a wrinkled old ear. In some old books it is called "Judas-ear", and has something to do with the Bible story. When Judas hanged himself it was supposed to be from this kind of tree.

Scrambling up the elderberry bush was a fine show of **White Convolvulus** or **Bindweed** in full bloom. This is also very unpopular with gardeners, but looks pleasant enough in the wild.

Crossing the burnt patch I knew what to expect—a fine show of **Rosebay**, the flower which did so well on the London bombed sites and likes burnt ground (see page 41). Here was another curious fungus, a toadstool called the **Inkcap** or **Lawyer's Wig.** It has a greyish-white cap which hangs down, and resembles what the judge wears in court. As it grows, a strange thing happens. Some chemical inside the toadstool slowly rots it away into a black, inky fluid. This was actually used years ago by writers when they used a quill pen. I have a piece of parchment on which I wrote some words with this ink twenty years ago. It is still quite clear.

Finally, the fallen tree. This was old and crumbling, and was once a fine **Elm** tree I remember as a boy. Now it was the home of many hidden insects and other small creatures. Most obvious was another fungus, this time a **Bracket** which grew out of the side of the old trunk called the **Dryad's Saddle.** It was a fine specimen, nearly 30 centimetres across, almost possible to sit on.

inkcap

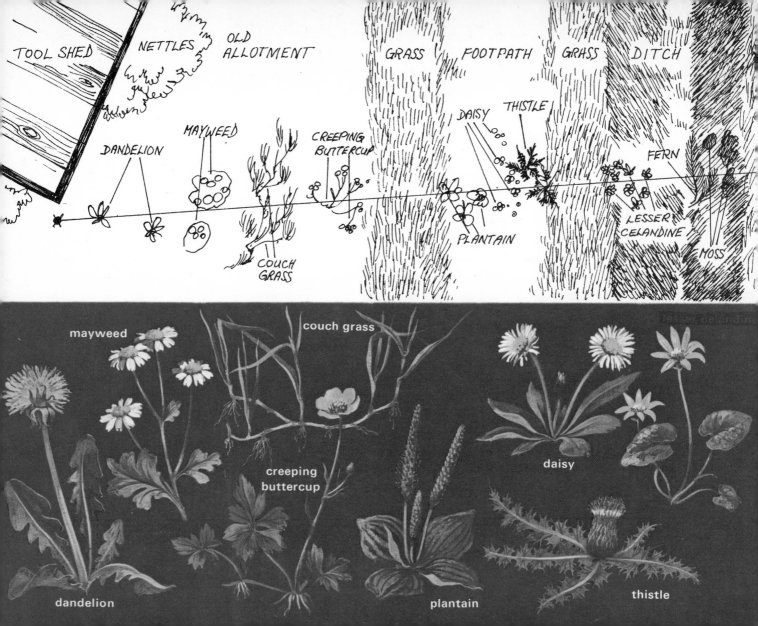

TOOL SHED | NETTLES | OLD ALLOTMENT | GRASS | FOOTPATH | GRASS | DITCH

DANDELION

MAYWEED

CREEPING BUTTERCUP

DAISY

THISTLE

FERN

COUCH GRASS

PLANTAIN

LESSER CELANDINE

MOSS

mayweed

couch grass

creeping buttercup

dandelion

plantain

daisy

thistle

GRASS

ELDERBERRY BUSH

JEWS EAR FUNGUS

BURNT PATCH

ROSEBAY

BURNT PATCH

INKCAP FUNGUS

DRYAD'S SADDLE

FALLEN TREE

NETTLES

male fern

convolvolus

rosebay willow herb

inkcap toadstool

Dryad's saddle fungus

"Jews Ear" fungus

moss

A SPIDER'S WEB

ONE OF THE most wonderful works of Nature is surely a spider's web. There is no more lovely sight on a summer's morning than a web covered in dewdrops. It looks like a necklace dripping with pearls.

This creation is the work of the **Garden Spider,** sometimes called the **Cross Spider** because it has a white cross on its back. It is the female who builds this orb web, and she does it purely by instinct. This complicated piece of architecture does not have to be learned.

There are plenty of places you can find such a web. It may be in your garden, in the town park or square, on some waste ground, or along a hedgerow. You may be lucky to catch a spider at work.

First, she spins a silk thread from the **spinneret** at the end of her body. This floats in the air, across a gap between the bushes, until it catches onto a branch on the other side. She pulls it tight, crosses over, and lowers herself on a second thread. In this way a rough circle is made which becomes the framework of the web. Now comes the complicated part, putting the "spokes" on the web, so that it resembles a kind of wheel. Starting from the centre, where all the spokes meet, she works her way outwards in a spiral which fills up the web.

This first spiral is only a guide-line. Now she works backwards towards the centre, gathering up this spiral, and putting another in its place. This second one is covered with a sticky substance. As this spiral is fixed to each spoke, the spider flicks it with her leg, as if twanging a guitar string. This causes the sticky substance to form into little globules, on which an unwary fly will later be caught.

Finally, when the job is finished, she spins a single thread which is fixed to the centre of the web, and carries it to a hidden place nearby. This thread acts as a kind of telegraph wire. Hidden behind a leaf, with her leg holding the thread, the spider can feel the slightest vibration on the web. This means that something has flown into it.

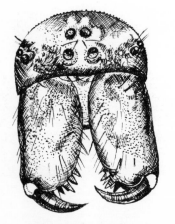

close-up of spider's head and jaws

Now comes the interesting part. If a tiny insect is caught, the vibration of its struggles are small, and the spider leaves it alone. If it is a normal-sized fly, she bites it, and wraps it up in silk. The bite contains poison, and the fly soon dies. If it is a large insect, such as a bumble-bee or beetle, she may decide to let it go and will cut it free.

I once tried an experiment. Borrowing a tuning fork from a music mistress I tapped it on my knee, and placed it against the web. Immediately the spider rushed out, probably thinking a fly had been caught. She did so four times and then stopped as if she knew I was fooling her. Actually, spiders cannot reason as we do, so it might have had something to do with the tuning fork. Perhaps the vibration was wrong. Insects move their wings at different speeds. For instance, a bee's wing-beat is 200 per second and a gnat's is 300.

Why not try to make a model of a spider's web? You will need some cotton or nylon thread, and a frame of wood to build it on. An old picture frame would do, or a forked branch to make it look more natural. Paint the threads with clear varnish to make them glisten.

Some people are scared of spiders, yet they will not attack you and most of them are harmless, so long as you do not touch them. Even those large, tropical spiders called **"Tarantulas"** need not be feared. Actually, the spiders which have a dangerous bite are rather small, such as the American **Black Widow Spider** and the **Sydney Funnel Spider** in Australia. The real **Tarantula** lives in the Mediterranean, and is only average-size. People once thought its bite was very serious. To get rid of the poison you had to go into a wild dance to sweat it out. Music was composed for this dance, which is called the Tarantella. It is usually small creatures like spiders and others which sting or bite that seem to frighten people. There was even a naturalist, a spider expert, who did not care for them, and wrote the nursery rhyme about his daughter "Little Miss Muffet sat on her tuffet . . ."

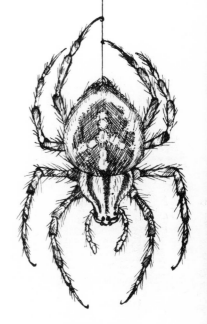

**garden or
cross spider**

tarantula

black
widow

garden or
cross spider

THE PEPPERED MOTH

BECAUSE EVERY kind of animal or plant has its own special character, such as size, shape, colour, and so on, we can tell a cat from a tiger, a mouse from a rabbit, or a buttercup from a daisy. Even so there is much variation within a single kind. Among humans no two are exactly alike, unless they happen to be identical twins. Among animals this ability to vary can be very important, and may even become a matter of life and death.

There is a famous example of this which has been discovered among insects which live in towns. A number of moths and ladybirds are turning much darker than usual in many places (see page 80). One of these is called the **Peppered Moth,** a common insect which lives among trees over much of Britain. Its wing-span is about 3½ centimetres across. They are pale-coloured and speckled with dark dots and lines. When they settle on a tree trunk to rest during the day, the moths blend perfectly with the lichens which normally grow on trees. You can also find them on rocks, walls and gravestones.

Lichens are primitive plants, a curious mixture of a fungus and an alga, and can live on bare surfaces without soil. But they must have clean air to grow in. The camouflage of the peppered moth is important to it, as otherwise sharp-eyed birds would see and catch it.

In 1848, outside Manchester, a black-coloured peppered moth was discovered. This happens now and then among animals, and is called **melanism,** meaning a very dark colouring, the opposite to an **albino** where the colours are missing.

At the beginning of this century melanic moths were a rarity, simply because they showed up against the tree trunks, and so were caught by the birds. There was roughly one black to every 99 normal moths in the country.

Since then there have been great changes in Britain. The history books call it the "Industrial Revolution". With the mining of coal used in our homes, factories and power stations, we started to pollute the countryside with smoke and other dirt. What were once clean country towns and villages are

robin

now inside great mining and industrial areas. Where this has happened, the lichens have been killed off and the trees covered in soot to make them dark.

This is where the black-coloured moths were at an advantage, for now they could hide against the trees. It was the normal, pale moths that showed up. Today, in polluted parts of Britain, the position is reversed, only about one normal moth to every 99 black. However, we still have clean places where the lichens can grow, especially in the West Country, Wales and Scotland. This is where you would probably find the normal moths. In the Midlands, the coal-mining areas, big towns like London, and much of eastern England, there are more black ones. It depends on where you happen to live what you would find on the trees around your home.

This distribution of normal and black moths is to do with the wind which usually blows across Britain, from the south-west. This means that much of the soot and grime is blown towards the east.

Today the smoke and fog is nothing like it used to be, when all the traffic came to a standstill in a filthy yellow smog, and you could hardly see a hand in front of your face.

Happily this is changing. If the Clean Air Act and the use of smokeless fuel is successful, then maybe the country will become a cleaner place. The lichens will return to grow on the trees, even inside towns, and the black moths will die out. I have searched many times for the peppered moth in London, but so far have only found the dark ones.

Why not do some searching where you live? Look on the tree trunks, fences and walls, and see if you can spot some. You could even try to breed some in a cage. Make a cage from a wooden box with a glass front and a roof of perforated zinc for ventilation. Some sprays of tree leaves, especially birch, will be eaten by the caterpillars when the eggs hatch out. Place the spray in a bottle of water to keep it fresh, and change it when necessary. Cover the top of the bottle so that the caterpillars do not crawl in and drown. A piece of bark would be useful for the moths to sit on.

NIGHT LIFE

As THE SUN goes down, and we arrive home from school or work, a different set of people go to work. The night watchman, the hospital nurses, the men in the factories and newspaper offices, take over the night shift as we go to bed.

It is the same with Nature. Animals of the night which we seldom see by day are awake and going about their business. They are taking over from the day animals.

There is something exciting about going outdoors after dark, and just listening to the different sounds. Just by standing still on the doorstep or in the garden you get a feeling that the world of nature is changing places. Even in town it is possible to notice this.

As the traffic dies down, you begin to hear sounds which are hidden during the day because of the noise. The siren of a police car or the sound of a train may be a long way off, but seems to come from the next road.

Then there are the sounds of nature. Sitting at the bedroom window one summer's night I made a note of all I heard. It was just after midnight, and there was a full moon shining over the lake opposite. The road was empty, and there was no traffic. An **Owl** started hooting in a nearby tree, and I could just make out its shape against the moon. Fluttering against the window was a large moth attracted by the lamplight, a handsome **Red Underwing.** When a window is open and the lights are on, night insects will sometimes fly in.

Next, a sleepy **Blackbird** started singing softly from the creeper against the house where it was roosting. Birds sometimes do this at night when they are disturbed.

There was an unusual noise of pattering feet, as if someone was running down the road in a hurry. It was a **Hedgehog** trotting down the middle of the road! It seems quite unconcerned, until I whistled. It stopped abruptly and curled up. This is why so many hedgehogs get run over at night. Normally when there is danger an animal will hide or run away, but a hedgehog rolls

blackbird

116

up and relies on its prickly coat for protection. This is useless against a heavy car. Maybe one day hedgehogs will learn curb drill. Have you ever seen a dog go up to a pedestrian crossing, sit down, and wait for the traffic to stop before crossing?

Against the moon I could see the bats flying about, chasing the moths. A bat has a remarkable way of doing this. Giving off a very high-pitched note it can pick this up as an echo. In this way it can avoid hitting anything, even though it can see. With this **echo-location,** or **sonar,** a bat can even track down an insect in mid-air. Some bats have a tail with a fold of skin on each side. This can be tucked between the hind legs, and used as a kind of shopping basket in which to place the insects they catch. A mother will also carry her baby when out hunting. The little one has special, hooked teeth for clinging onto her fur.

A dog barked in the distance, a sharp, yapping bark repeated three times. This was no ordinary bark, but the call of a **dog fox.** Foxes are not unusual in the suburbs of large towns these days.

fox barking

Early morning, just before dawn, is a good time to wake up and sit by the window, especially if there are gardens or a park nearby. All is quiet, then suddenly a blackbird, song-thrush, or maybe a robin starts to sing. It works almost like an alarm clock. Within minutes the air is full of bird-song. This is the **Dawn Chorus,** when all the cock birds sing in May or during June. It takes place every year when the birds are nesting.

It used to be thought that male birds sing in order to attract a mate. This is certainly true, but there is another reason. The song is a way of telling all the other male birds that the singer has found a place for a nest, and not to interfere. It is a kind of battle-cry, and means "this is my bush or tree, so keep off". All the male birds are challenging one another, and getting their nests sorted out. If you are good at imitating bird song you can sometimes get a male bird to reply.

fox

THE ROMANCE OF FLOWERS

bluebell

There is romance just around the corner, if you only care to look, even inside a town. Notice the familiar wildflowers which appear every summer in odd corners, and in very artificial surroundings. You will find blossoms along the roadside verge, on the village green, along the ditch, in the car park by the station, and along the railway line.

These familiar flowers, often called **weeds** by gardeners, are taken so much for granted, that we seem to forget that they have a real beauty of their own. Some of their names are very old and romantic. Here are some of the flowers which we have already met and their names.

The little **Daisy** was named by our ancestors in Saxon times, and called the *daeg's-eye*. It means the "eye of the day" because a daisy opens its petals in daytime when it is sunny and closes them in dull weather and at night. The **Dandelion,** from the French words *"dents-de-lion"*, means "lion's teeth". It may have got its name from the shape of the leaves, or the colour of the flowers. It is really a beautiful plant and, if it was rare, gardeners might want to grow it. As it is, we grab it up, or gather the leaves to feed the tortoise. At one time the dandelion was of great importance. In those early days the doctors, called **herbalists,** were also good botanists. They studied the wild flowers to see whether their juices could be used as a medicine, and the dandelion was one of them.

The lovely dandelion "clock" it produces is worth a close look. Its tiny parachute seeds get carried away by the wind, so no wonder it is widespread (see page 98).

The **Plantain** is another common "weed" which grows on wasteland or on a neglected path or lawn. Its old name was **Waybread.** This was a mistake because one herbalist spelled it wrongly. It should really be "Waybroad," that is, a plant that grows by the broad wayside. Wherever people walk they pick up the little nuts on their shoes and spread them along the roads and pathways. The **Hawthorn** or **May Tree,** which forms hedges and is common around fields and in town parks, has a long connection with religion. Have you ever heard someone say that it is unlucky to bring May blossom into the house? This is because the Romans chose the flower as a symbol for their pagan goddess, Maia. The month of May is named after her. The early Christians thought it wrong to bring this flower into their homes and churches, because it had to do with paganism.

Many flowers have been given names by the herbalists to remind the simple folk that they could be used for healing various kinds of illness. Two of these often seen in town parks and nearby woods are the **Self-heal** and the **Wound-wort.** The names speak for themselves. In those early days there were no chemists and few doctors, so people collected wild plants to make their own medicine.

The **Foxglove,** grown in gardens and often seen wild, is a good example of a plant still used for illness. The seeds contain a drug called **digitalin** which helps people with heart trouble. In fact, the plant's scientific name is **Digitalis.** The name "Foxglove" is puzzling, but it could have been called "Folk's glove", that is, the flowers worn as gloves by the "little folk". So perhaps if you grow foxgloves there may be fairies at the bottom of your garden after all!

Here is just one legend which has been handed down from Ancient Greece. It is over two thousand years old, and about a common flower which can be seen in parks and gardens or close to towns in the woods—the **Bluebell.** It is also called the **Wild Hyacinth,** a cousin of our garden hyacinths.

One day the sun god Apollo was playing with a young man, called Hyacinth, throwing the discus. Watching nearby was another, very jealous god of the West Wind, called Zephyrus. As the boy threw the discus, Zephyrus huffed and puffed a mighty wind, so that the discus hit the boy on the head and killed him. Apollo was grief-striken and so that the boy should always be remembered he named after him a little flower that was growing beside his lifeless body.

foxglove